Making Mobile Hen Houses

by

Michael Roberts

Edited by Sara Roadnight

Photographs and drawings

by

Michael Roberts

Published by Gold Cockerel Books

ISBN 0947870 466

CONDITIONS OF SALE

Foreword

This book is a sequel to 'Poultry House Construction', my first book on poultry housing, and ideally should be read in conjunction with it.

I have added a number of new ideas in this book including, of course, poultry house mobility as well as roll-away nestboxes and a hen house for wheel-chair users. I must thank my good friend Nigel Woodrup (of 'Sheep for Beginners' fame) for his helpful ideas and comments on this one.

Another important new project is the sound moderated house, possibly a first in the poultry world, and one that I would not have thought about had it not been for a farmer neighbour who complained about my cockerels!

This book might have appeared a few months earlier if I had not been involved in a nasty accident which left me with 5 broken ribs, a broken collar bone and a shoulder blade broken in three places, all on the right side of course! This rather slowed me down (!!) but the period of convalescence has given me time for further reflection and may have produced a better book as a result. During my absence from the workshop, Jim Macfarlane and Pete Hawthorne kindly came in and constructed several of the houses, for which I am very grateful.

I have not suggested any time scale for production as everyone works at different speeds.

I hope you enjoy making these houses. A great deal of thought has gone into them as I have tried to ensure that they are fairly simple and straightforward to construct, easy to clean, poultry friendly and not bad looking either.

Michael Roberts
Kennerleigh, 2004

CONTENTS

POINTS TO REMEMBER WHEN BUYING A NEW HEN HOUSE

When I see the poor design of some of the poultry houses on sale today I feel it's not surprising that people sometimes have problems with their birds. Here are some points to look out for.

Perches

Perches too narrow, 1" or 1.5" wide. Perches must be 2" wide although 1.5" is adequate for small bantams like Sebrights. Make sure that the top corners of the perch are beveled.

Fixed perches: these are often nailed or screwed to the wall of the house, a common mistake. All perches must be easily removable.

Perches the same height as, or lower than nestboxes. I see this time and time again and it always results in the hens roosting (and messing) in the nestboxes. Some 'clever' manufacturers put screens in to stop this happening but these have to be lowered every day to prevent birds from roosting in the wrong place, rather inconvenient for a busy person.

Wrong position of perches: all too often perches are put in front of nestboxes with no droppings board underneath. This means that hens have to walk through their own droppings to get into the nestbox and will almost certainly contaminate the eggs when they get there.

Wrong spacing of perches: the spacing needs to be correct for the breed of bird and will obviously vary according to size.

Nestboxes

The most important point about nestboxes is good access, for cleaning, for collecting eggs and for observation. The best access is from above so that you have a clear view inside to look out for any broken eggs or red mite. The lid of the nestbox must be carefully constructed to prevent rain from getting in and making the shavings or straw wet. It's important that there is plenty of room inside so that the hen can move round easily, and also enough depth for a good thick layer of nesting material . There has been a debate for a long time about the merits of individual or communal nestboxes, but in the end it's a personal choice. I prefer communal ones as they are easier to clean out, and providing I use best shavings about 3" deep, there are few broken eggs.

Popholes

These must be the right size; if they are too small the cockerels particularly will have difficulty squeezing in and out; if they are too big the house will get wet and draughty. The opening and closing device must be fox proof and not liable to shut if it is nudged by a bird's back. There may need to be a ramp or step up to the pophole on the outside of the house.

Ventilation

You must be able to control the ventilation according to the weather and the time of year. This is done with a sliding shutter which can be opened in the summer and almost closed during cold, wet or windy periods. Good ventilation is very important but the house should not be draughty.

Light

Natural light is all important if the house is not lit artificially, as hens need it to stimulate the laying process. Wall light is better than roof light as birds will not perch under a sky light, so always opt for windows in the wall rather than Perspex in the roof. The ventilation shutter can be incorporated with the window.

Access

Easy access to the inside of the house and nestbox is vital as it will speed up and improve the business of cleaning, making it less of a chore. It's no fun if you have to kneel down in the mud or wet grass to get your hen house clean.

Suitable construction materials

Most houses are constructed of wood, normally plyboard, shiplap, tongue and groove or feather edge. Some poultry house manufacturers cut corners by using wafer board and chip board, neither of which is suitable for interior or exterior use; they absorb water, swell and eventually crumble.

Wood treatments

This is an individual choice although it's best to construct housing with treated wood which will have more durability and give the house a longer life span. If you decide on untreated timber you will have to treat the wood with either an oil based preservative or a water based solution. Not to treat the wood at all would be to throw money away.

Oil based preservatives are better for use on houses that will be static or on the ground for long periods such as arks, runs or fold units. Water based preservatives work well on houses that are raised off the ground on bricks or concrete blocks.

Types of wheel used in this book. 14"ø pneumatic barrow wheel with 1" axle, and solid rubber and plastic sheep trough wheel 10½"ø with 1" axle.

WHEEL ASSEMBLIES

Hinge under wheels

This design is best used on light arks, runs and fold units. There are three positions:

    a) the wheels at rest with the ark/run on the ground,
    b) the ark/run sitting on the assembly supports for cleaning,
    c) the wheels hinged under the ark/run ready for moving.

You have to lift the ark/run and kick the wheel assembly into the position you need with your foot.

Wheel lowered

Wheel raised

Hinge under wheels

Wheels on stand

Wheel assembly

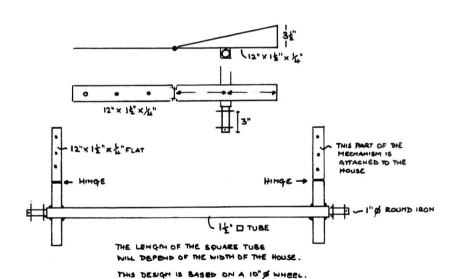

$3\frac{1}{2}$"

$(12" \times 1\frac{1}{2}" \times \frac{1}{4}")$

$12" \times 1\frac{1}{2}" \times \frac{1}{4}"$

3"

$12" \times 1\frac{1}{2}" \times \frac{1}{4}"$ FLAT

← HINGE   HINGE →

THIS PART OF THE MECHANISM IS ATTACHED TO THE HOUSE

1" ⌀ ROUND IRON

$1\frac{1}{2}"$ ☐ TUBE

THE LENGTH OF THE SQUARE TUBE WILL DEPEND OF THE WIDTH OF THE HOUSE.

THIS DESIGN IS BASED ON A 10" ⌀ WHEEL.

Lift and hook wheels

This system is for light houses or fold units, etc. The two wheels are attached to a round metal bar or axle. Lift the house and guide the wheels so that the axle fits under the 'hooks' at the bottom of the house. Once the bar or axle is located, go to the other end of the unit, lift and push it like a wheelbarrow. This is a cheap and easy method of moving different types and widths of house and run.

Wheels hooked up

Wheels detached

Wheel hooks

Lift and hook wheels using wooden hooks

Lift and hook wheels

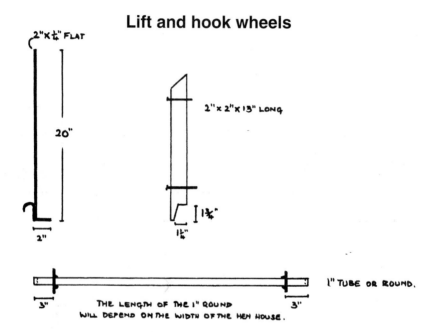

2"x ¼" FLAT

20"

2"

2" x 2" x 13" LONG

1¾"

1¼"

1" TUBE OR ROUND.

3"   THE LENGTH OF THE 1" ROUND   3"
WILL DEPEND ON THE WIDTH OF THE HEN HOUSE.

Dolly carriage wheels

This wheel assembly is for heavier houses or fold units where there are several of the same design. The dolly is wheeled up to the house and located on the pick-up points, then the handle is pushed down, raising it up. At this stage you need a strong pole or board to insert under the end of the house, resting on the dolly's frame either side. The house can then be wheeled round by hand or moved by a tractor. The trick when putting this assembly together is to locate the pick up points as near as possible to the centre of balance.

Dolly carriage assembly

Metal lifting frame fixed permanently to house

15

House raised on dolly carriage

House on the ground

16

Raising the house with the dolly carriage by pushing down on the bar before inserting the wooden plank.

House ready to be moved.

I designed and made these houses as part of a special order for free range poultry housing. Each one was 14ft long and 6ft wide and could be moved either by hand or by a small tractor. The wheels on this dolly were taken from a Mini car.

Dolly carriage wheels

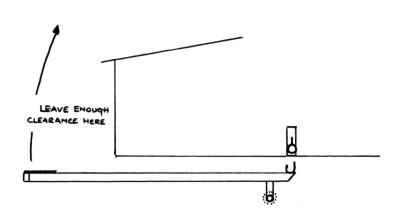

LEAVE ENOUGH
CLEARANCE HERE

THIS AXLE PIECE IS FASTENED TO THE
UNDERNEATH OF THE HOUSE.

(2" x ⅛" FLAT

GUSSET

I 1½" — 1" x 2⅛" LONG TUBE

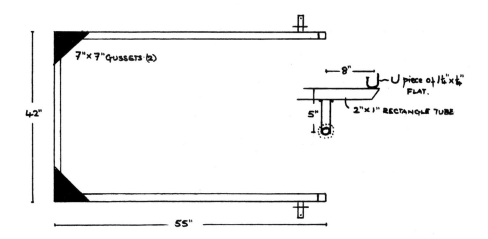

7" x 7" GUSSETS (2)

42"

55"

8"

U piece of 1½" x ¼"
FLAT.

5"

2" x 1" RECTANGLE TUBE

Jack-down wheels

These are normally fixed to fold units and each side is raised and lowered by a lever. They are very easy to operate.

Details of jack down wheel assembly.

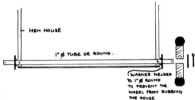

HEN HOUSE

1" ∅ TUBE OR ROUND.

WASHER WELDED
TO 1" ∅ ROUND
TO PREVENT THE
WHEEL FROM RUBBING
THE HOUSE

JACK DOWN WHEELS.

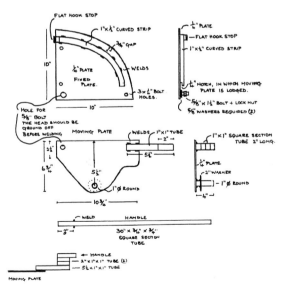

FLAT HOOK STOP

1" x ¼" CURVED STRIP

¾" GAP

WELDS

FIXED PLATE.

¹⁄₁₆" PLATE

10"

3 x ¼" BOLT HOLES.

10"

⅛" PLATE

FLAT HOOK STOP

1" x ¼" CURVED STRIP

¹⁄₁₆" NOTCH, IN WHICH MOVING PLATE IS LODGED.

⅝" x 1½" BOLT + LOCK NUT
⅝" WASHERS REQUIRED (2)

HOLE FOR
⅝" BOLT
THE HEAD SHOULD BE
GROUND OFF
BEFORE WELDING

MOVING PLATE

WELDS

1"x1" TUBE

2"

5½"

2¼"

6³⁄₁₆"

5½"

1" ∅ ROUND

10³⁄₁₆"

1"x1" SQUARE SECTION
TUBE 2" LONG.

⅛" PLATE

2" WASHER

1" ∅ ROUND

4"

WELD

HANDLE

2"

30" x ¾" x ¾"
SQUARE SECTION
TUBE

HANDLE

2"x1"x1" TUBE (2)

5½"x1"x1" TUBE

MOVING PLATE

21

Barrow type wheel

This assembly is permanently fixed to smaller fold units or broody coops, etc. and the unit is picked up and pushed along on one wheel. It is a very simple design but must be securely bolted to the frame of the unit.

View of barrow type wheel.

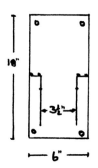

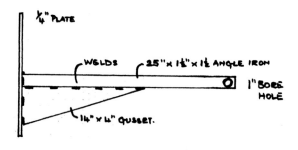

Fixed wheels

This kind of wheel assembly is fixed permanently to the house/fold unit which is built around it. When the unit is lifted it clears the ground for mobility. The design of this type of fold unit must be carefully thought out to ensure that it is fox-proof.

View of fixed wheels.

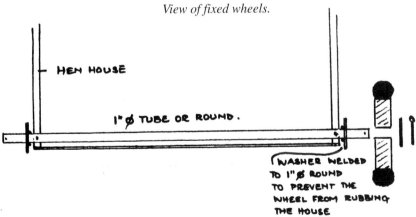

HEN HOUSE

1" ⌀ TUBE OR ROUND.

WASHER WELDED TO 1" ⌀ ROUND TO PREVENT THE WHEEL FROM RUBBING THE HOUSE

This method of mobility can be fixed anywhere on the hen house. The nearer to the end, the greater the lifting clearance, but the heavier the weight.

Trolley wheels

These are used on small hen or duck houses and consist of a frame with a pair of wheels attached.

Trolley wheel assembly

Trolley wheel assembly with house.

Trolley wheels

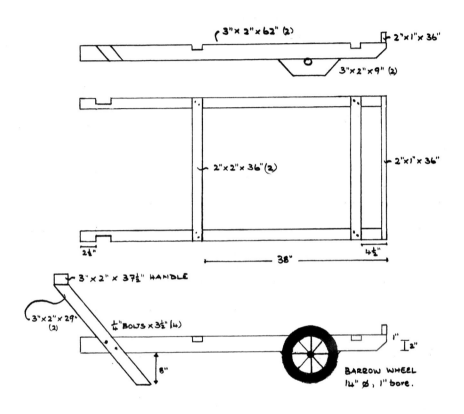

3"× 2"× 62" (2)

2"×1"× 36"

3"× 2"×9" (2)

2"×2"×36" (2)

2"×1"× 36"

2¼"

38"

4½"

3"× 2"× 37½" HANDLE

3"× 2"× 29" (2)

¼" BOLTS × 3½" (4)

8"

1"

2"

BARROW WHEEL
14" Ø, 1" bore.

SLEDGE

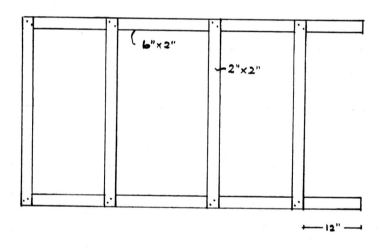

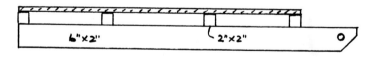

I have deliberately left out the overall sizes as they will be governed by the floor size of the house. The floor must be fixed to the skid frame to give the construction strength and rigidity. Countersink the floor screws or nails to avoid catching them when cleaning out the house.

BROODY COOP

There is a multi-functional broody coop in my other housing book 'Poultry House Construction'. I have improved that design so that access is now a lot better and the coop is lighter to carry. It has been used regularly and works well.

The accommodation has a hinged roof which folds back to rest on the run so that the internal section (which has the pop hole in it) can be lifted out, making cleaning very easy. There is a unique pivoting door on the outside of the pop hole to shut the broody and chicks in the house area.

The top of the run lifts and slides out allowing total access inside, and the front divider (or end of the run) can be removed to allow the birds their freedom. There is a catch on the handle of the coop by the hinged roof to prevent the wind or a fox from lifting it.

I have used this coop with three broods of chicks, Silkies and Welsummers, and it has worked well; it's also very easy to build.

Broody coop.

27

Broody coop showing access.

Front view of broody coop.

Detail of removable middle section.

Broody coop

SIDE VIEW

$5\frac{1}{8}$" $5\frac{1}{4}$"

A

WIRE MESH PANEL
36" x 16" x 1"

C   C   C

B

A = 68" x 2" x 1" (2)
B = 57½ x 2" x 1" (2)
C = 16" x 2" x 1" (6)
D = 22" x 2" x 1" (6)

TOP VIEW

$\frac{3}{16}$" GAP   A

D ~ D (see DIAGRAM OF FRONT SECTION)   D

BASE VIEW

B

D   11" x 2" x 1" DOOR STOP   11" x 2" x 1"   D   D

2" ⌐ 1" x $\frac{5}{8}$"
        1"

$\frac{1}{2}$" PLY DOOR

2" ⊔ DOOR STOP
1" 1"

18½"

$3\frac{3}{16}$"

$2\frac{1}{2}$"

21"   SIDE PANEL   17½"

$20\frac{1}{16}$"

BACK PANEL   24"

17¼"

FLOOR   1"

2"

18½"

29

Broody coop continued

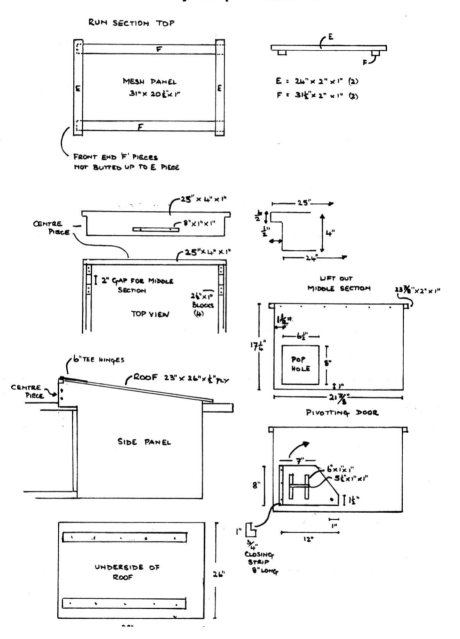

RUN SECTION TOP

MESH PANEL
31" × 20½" × 1"

FRONT END 'F' PIECES
NOT BUTTED UP TO E PIECE

E = 26" × 2" × 1" (2)
F = 31½" × 2" × 1" (2)

CENTRE PIECE

25" × 4" × 1"
8" × 1" × 1"
25" × 4" × 1"

2" GAP FOR MIDDLE SECTION

26" × 1" BLOCKS (4)

TOP VIEW

LIFT OUT MIDDLE SECTION

23⅜" × 2" × 1"

POP HOLE

PIVOTTING DOOR

6" TEE HINGES
ROOF 23" × 26" × ¼" PLY

CENTRE PIECE

SIDE PANEL

6" × 1" × 1"
5½" × 1" × 1"

CLOSING STRIP 8" LONG

UNDERSIDE OF ROOF

26"

Broody coop continued

FRONT SECTION

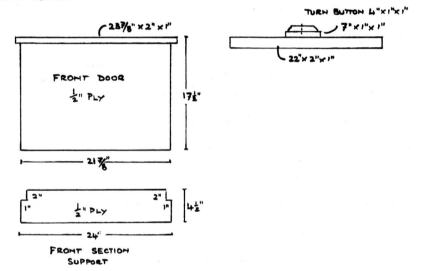

23⅜" × 2" × 1"

FRONT DOOR
½" PLY

17½"

21⅞"

TURN BUTTON 4" × 1" × 1"

7" × 1" × 1"

22" × 2" × 1"

2"   2"
1"   ½" PLY   1"

4½"

24"

FRONT SECTION
SUPPORT

BANTAM FOLD UNIT

It's not essential to use wheels with this house but if you wish to, the lift and hook ones work well. There are several design features which include a completely fold-down front, a removable top to the run section and fox-proof locks on all the top sections. This unit can be used for rearing as well as for laying birds and can be quickly dismantled for cleaning.

Bantam fold unit showing access.

Interior of bantam fold unit.

Bantam fold unit

SIDES

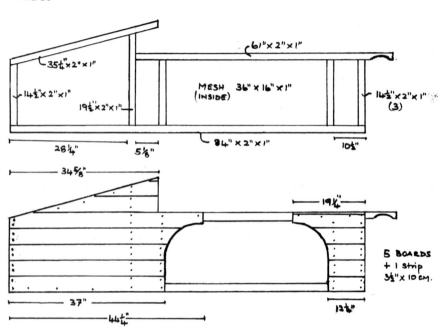

35¼" x 2" x 1"

61" x 2" x 1"

14½" x 2" x 1"

19½" x 2" x 1"

MESH 36" x 16" x 1"
(INSIDE)

14½" x 2" x 1"
(3)

28¼"

5⅝"

84" x 2" x 1"

10½"

34⅝"

19¼"

5 BOARDS
+ 1 strip
3½" x 10 cm.

37"

12½"

44¼"

MIDDLE SECTION

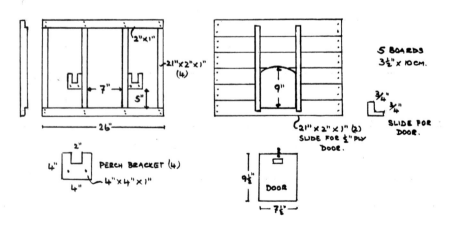

2" x 1"

21" x 2" x 1"
(4)

7"

5"

26"

9"

5 BOARDS
3½" x 10 cm.

¾"
¾"

SLIDE FOR
DOOR.

2"

4"

PERCH BRACKET (4)

4"   4" x 4" x 1"

21" x 2" x 1" (2)
SLIDE FOR ½" PLY
DOOR.

9½"

DOOR

7½"

34

Bantam fold unit continued

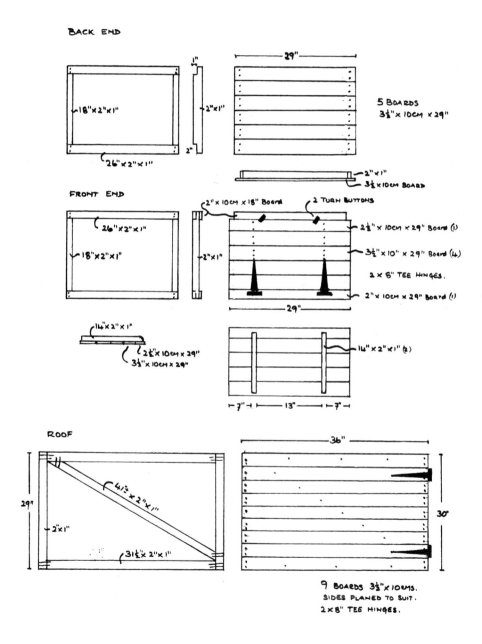

BACK END

18"x2"x1"
2"x1"
26"x2"x1"
1"
2"
29"

5 BOARDS
3½"x 10CM x 29"

2"x1"
3½x10CM BOARD

FRONT END

26"x2"x1"
18"x2"x1"
2"x1"

2"x 10CM x 18" Board   2 TURN BUTTONS
2½" x 10CM x 29" Board (1)
3½" x 10" x 29" Board (4)
2 x 6" TEE HINGES.
2" x 10CM x 29" Board (1)
29"

14"x2"x1"
2½"x 10CM x 29"
3½"x 10CM x 29"

14"x2"x1" (2)

7"   13"   7"

ROOF

29"
4/3 x 2"x 1"
2"x1"
31½x 2"x1"

36"
30"

9 BOARDS 3½"x 10CMS.
SIDES PLANED TO SUIT.
2 x 6" TEE HINGES.

35

Bantam fold unit continued

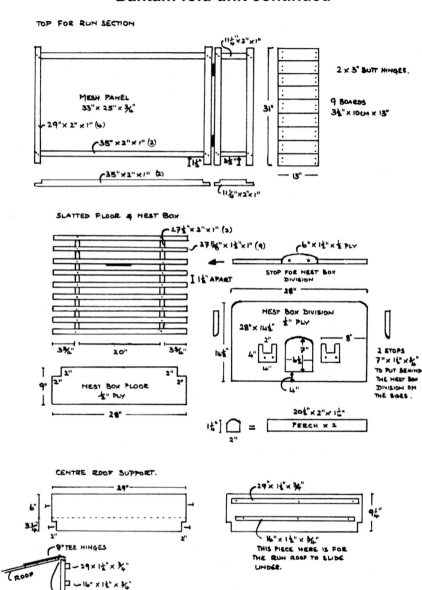

TOP FOR RUN SECTION

11¼"x 2"x 1"

MESH PANEL
33" x 25" x 3/16"

2 x 3" BUTT HINGES.

29"x 2" x 1" (4)

9 BOARDS
3½"x 10cm x 13"

35"x 2"x 1" (2)

31"

1½"   2½"

35"x 2"x 1" (2)

13"

11½"x 2"x 1"

SLATTED FLOOR & NEST BOX

27½"x 2"x 1" (2)

27⅝"x 1½"x 1" (9)

6"x 1½"x ½" PLY

STOP FOR NEST BOX
DIVISION

1½" APART

28"

NEST BOX DIVISION
28" x 14½"   ½" PLY

2"   7"   8"

4"   4½"

4"

2 STOPS
7"x 1½"x ½"
TO PUT BEHIND
THE NEST BOX
DIVISION ON
THE SIDES.

3¾"   20"   3¾"

9"   2"   2"   2"   2"
NEST BOX FLOOR
½" PLY

28"

20½"x 2"x 1¼"
PERCH x 2

1½"   2"

CENTRE ROOF SUPPORT.

29"

6"
3½"   2"   2"

29"x 1½"x ¾"

16"x 1½"x ¾"
THIS PIECE HERE IS FOR
THE RUN ROOF TO SLIDE
UNDER.

9¼"

9"TEE HINGES

29x 1½"x ¾"

16"x 1½"x ¾"

NOTE ANGLE.
TO ALLOW ROOF TO FOLD
BACK ONTO RUN.

ROOF

Bantam fold unit continued

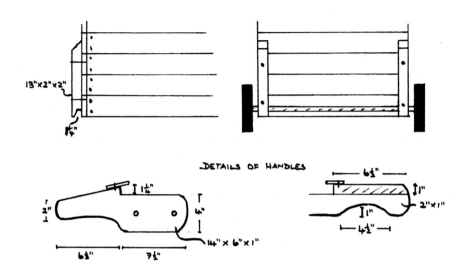

13"×2"×2"

1¼"

DETAILS OF HANDLES

1¼"

2"

4"

6½"

7½"

14" × 6" × 1"

6½"

1"

2"×1"

1"

4½"

LARGE FOLD UNIT

This fold unit is best used with wheels, and works well with either dolly carriage or jack-down ones. It provides height and space for 4 to 6 larger birds and is easy to manage. There is provision for an undercover food hopper and a platform for a drinker as well as shelter for the birds on cold frosty mornings. The laying and roosting area can be quickly dismantled for cleaning, and there is a fox-proof catch on the front pop hole.

Large fold unit showing access.

Perches and slatted floor.

Nest box and perches.

Front section with fox-proof catch.

Front section with pop hole door open.

Platform in run section.

Sliding door on middle section.

Large fold unit

SIDE

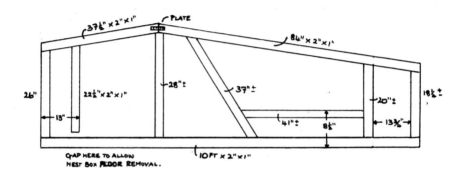

37½" x 2" x 1"

PLATE

84" x 2" x 1"

26"

22½" x 2" x 1"

13"

28" ±

37" ±

41" ±

8½"

20" ±

13⅜"

18⅜" ±

GAP HERE TO ALLOW NEST BOX FLOOR REMOVAL.

10 FT x 2" x 1"

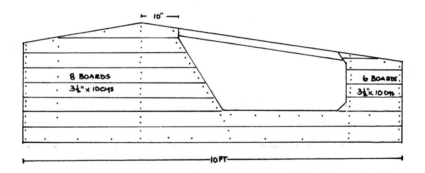

10"

8 BOARDS
3½" x 10 CMS

6 BOARDS
3½" x 10 CMS

10 FT

BACK END.

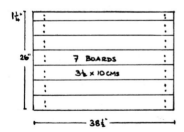

1½"

26"

7 BOARDS

3½ x 10 CMS

38¼"

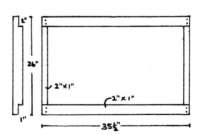

2"

26"

2" x 1"

2" x 1"

1"

35½"

42

Large fold unit continued

FRONT END.

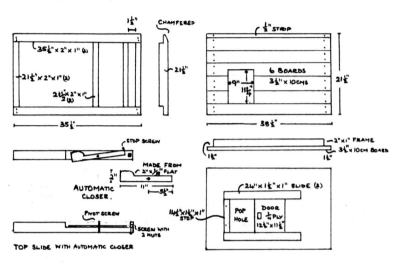

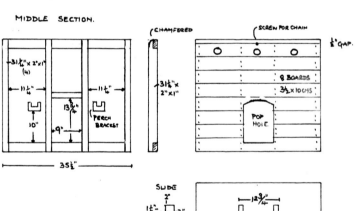

MIDDLE SECTION.

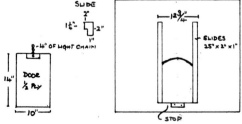

43

Large fold unit continued

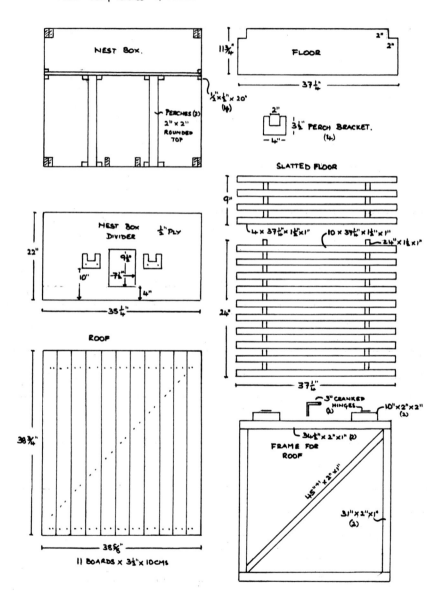

NEST BOX, PERCHES & FLOOR

NEST BOX.

PERCHES (2)
2" x 2"
ROUNDED
TOP

½" x ½" x 20"
(4)

FLOOR

11¾"

2"
2"

37¼"

2"
3½" PERCH BRACKET.
(4)
4"

NEST BOX
DIVIDER   ½" PLY

22"

10"   7½"

9½"

4"

35¼"

SLATTED FLOOR

9"

24"

4 x 37¼" x 1½" x 1"   10 x 37¼" x 1½" x 1"   24" x 1½" x 1"

37¼"

ROOF

38¾"

38⅝"
11 BOARDS x 3½" x 10cms

3" CRANKED
HINGES
(6)

10" x 2" x 2"
(2)

34½" x 2" x 1" (2)
FRAME FOR
ROOF

45¾" x 2" x 1"

31" x 2" x 1"
(2)

44

Large fold unit continued

ROOF FOR RUN SECTION.

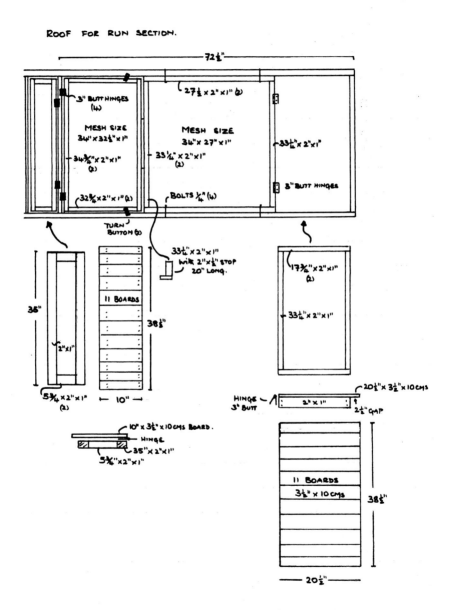

35"

5 3/4" x 2" x 1" (2)

2" x 1"

11 BOARDS

38 1/2"

72 1/2"

3" BUTT HINGES (4)

MESH SIZE 34" x 32 1/2" x 1"

34 3/8" x 2" x 1" (2)

32 5/8" x 2" x 1" (2)

TURN BUTTON (2)

27 1/2 x 2" x 1" (2)

MESH SIZE 34" x 27" x 1"

33 1/2" x 2" x 1" (2)

BOLTS 1/4" (4)

33 1/4" x 2" x 1"

3" BUTT HINGES

33 1/4" x 2" x 1" with 2" x 1 1/4" STOP 20" LONG.

17 3/8" x 2" x 1" (2)

33 1/4" x 2" x 1"

10" →

10" x 3 1/2" x 10 cms BOARD.
HINGE
35" x 2" x 1"

5 3/4" x 2" x 1"

HINGE — 3" BUTT

20 1/4" x 3 1/2" x 10 cms

2" x 1"

2 1/4" GAP

11 BOARDS
3 1/2" x 10 cms

38 1/2"

20 1/2"

FIXED WHEEL FOLD UNIT

This type of wheeled unit has its pros and cons. It's very convenient to have wheels already attached that don't have to be moved up and down or otherwise manipulated, but the ground clearance under this house is never very great, and if the wheels are positioned too close to the back it can be very heavy to lift.

This fold unit is constructed of 2" x 1" batten and .5" tongue and groove timber. I have tried to make it as strong as I can without it becoming a dead weight. There is good access all round, the nestbox being at the back of the covered area. All the inside fittings such as perches, nestbox parts, etc. lift out for easy cleaning.

Fixed wheel fold unit.

Fixed wheel fold unit.

Interior of fold unit.

47

Fixed wheel fold unit

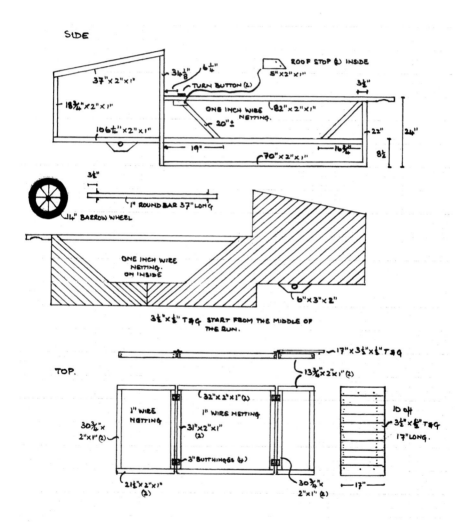

SIDE

ROOF STOP (2) INSIDE
5"x2"x1"

3⅜"
6¼"

37"x2"x1"
TURN BUTTON (2)
3½"

18¾"x2"x1"
ONE INCH WIRE
NETTING.
82"x2"x1"

106½"x2"x1"
20"±

19"
70"x2"x1"
16¾"
22"
24"

8½"

3½"

1" ROUND BAR 37" LONG

14" BARROW WHEEL

ONE INCH WIRE
NETTING.
ON INSIDE

6"x3"x2"

3½"x⅝" T&G START FROM THE MIDDLE OF
THE RUN.

17"x3½"x⅝" T&G

13¾"x2"x1" (2)

TOP.

32"x2"x1" (2)

1" WIRE
NETTING

1" WIRE NETTING

30¾"x
2"x1" (2)

31"x2"x1"
(2)

3" BUTT HINGES (4)

10 off
3½"x⅝" T&G
17"LONG.

21½"x2"x1"
(2)

30¾"x
2"x1" (2)

17"

48

Fixed wheel fold unit continued

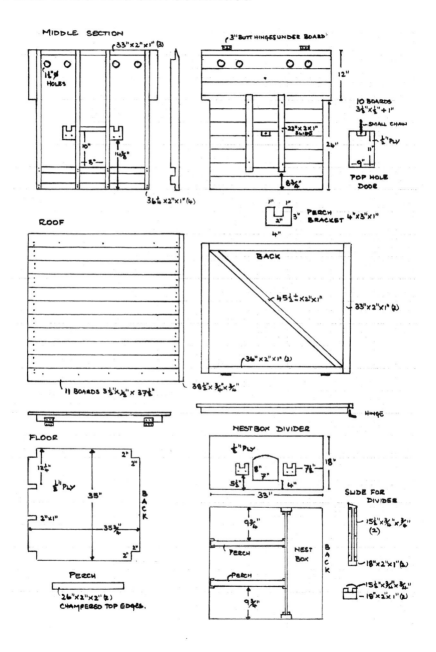

Fixed wheel fold unit continued

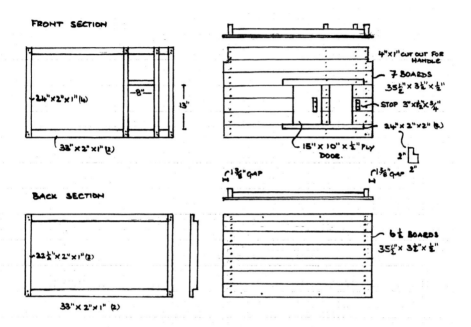

FRONT SECTION

24"x2"x1" (4)

33"x2"x1" (2)

8"

13"

4"x1" CUT OUT FOR HANDLE

7 BOARDS
35½"x 3½"x ½"

STOP 3"x1½x¾"

24"x 2"x2" (2)

15"x 10"x ½" PLY DOOR.

1⅜" GAP

2"

1⅜" GAP 2"

BACK SECTION

22½"x 2"x1" (2)

33"x 2"x1" (2)

6½ BOARDS
35½"x 3½"x ½"

DUCK HOUSE

Ducks don't like being shut up at night, they would far rather stay out near a pond, so having to drive them into a house every evening can sometimes be very tedious. When a duck is being driven it's always watching you out of the corner of one eye so it will often cannon into any troughs or feeders that happen to be lying about.

This house is very easy to clean as all you need to do is slide the roof open and lean in from the top to scrape it out. The ventilation is covered so that the ducks won't be able to glimpse any light outside which could make them panic. I have used an iron rod as a hinge for the ramp as I

Duck house on wheels

have found over the years that the standard tee hinge wears out quickly and breaks with the accumulation of mud and muck that collects from the ducks' feet.

Try to position the house alongside a fence or fix a wire fencing section next to it; you'll find it much easier to drive the ducks inside if they can run along by the fence and up the ramp. Without this you could spend a considerable part of the evening going round and round the field after your ducks!

It's a good idea to raise the house up about 6" to prevent rats from nesting underneath.

Duck house on ground with door open.

Duck house showing access.

Duck house showing detail of ramp.

Duck house

FRONT.

48"

48" x 2" x 1"

34½" x 3½" HOLE
MESH ON INSIDE
36" x 5" x 1"

36"

22"

11¼" x 1" x 1"

20"

½" PLY.

13" x 2" x 2"

10½"

1½"

1½" gap   2½"

24" x 2" x 2"

11½"

RAMP & DOOR.

HOLE

15½" x 2" x 2"

24" x 2" x 2" (2)

30" x 2" x 1"

22" x 6" (14CM) x 1" (2)

HANDLE
5½" x 1" x 1"

POP
HOLE

18"

1½" x 1" (2)
NOTCHED
FOR ROD.

16½" x ⅝" IRON ROD
WASHERS & PINS

½" GAP BETWEEN
HOLE AND 2" x 2"

4½"

3½"

44" x 6" (14CM) x 1"

HOLE COVER.

1"
THICK

4½"

3½"

54

Duck house continued

SLIDING ROOF

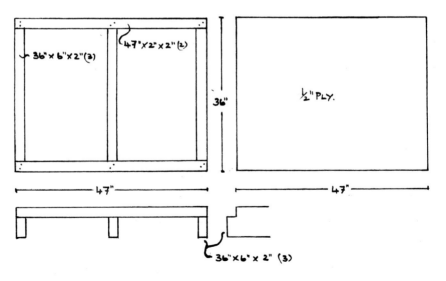

½" PLY

45"

52" x 3" x 1"

75°

41" x 3" x 1"
(2)

52½" x 2" x 1"

52½"

38" x 1" x 1½" (2)

41" x 3" x 1" (2)

½" PLY

BASE

36" x 6" x 2" (3)

47" x 2" x 2" (2)

36"

½" PLY.

47"

47"

36" x 6" x 2" (3)

Duck house continued

SIDES.

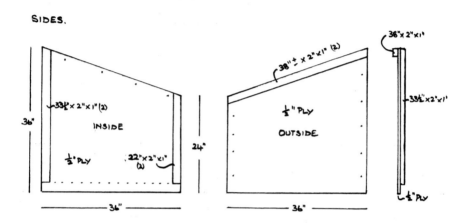

- 38" ± x 2" x 1" (2)
- 33½" x 2" x 1" (2)
- INSIDE
- ½" PLY
- 22" x 2" x 1" (2)
- 36"
- 36"
- ½" PLY
- OUTSIDE
- 24"
- 36"
- 36" x 2" x 1"
- 33½" x 2" x 1"
- ½" PLY

BACK.

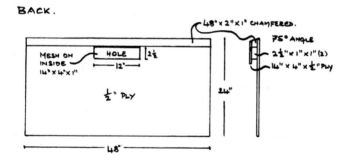

- MESH ON INSIDE 16" x 4" x 1"
- HOLE
- 12"
- 2½
- ½" PLY
- 48" x 2" x 1" CHAMFERED.
- 75° ANGLE
- 2½" x 1" x 1" (2)
- 16" x 4" x ½" PLY
- 24"
- 48"

4FT X 3FT HEN HOUSE

This is a very simple house to make and I'm sure could be completed in a weekend. It can be tailor made for any size of hen or bantam as the pop hole can be enlarged or the perch brackets moved, and the nestbox is large enough to cope with most breeds.

Front of 4' x 3' hen house.

The roof slides on and off and incorporates a vent on each side at the top. This means that if necessary, the louvre on the front of the house can be shut down completely and there will still be sufficient ventilation for the birds inside.

Detail of access.

Detail of nest box

Detail of pop hole.

4ft x 3ft hen house

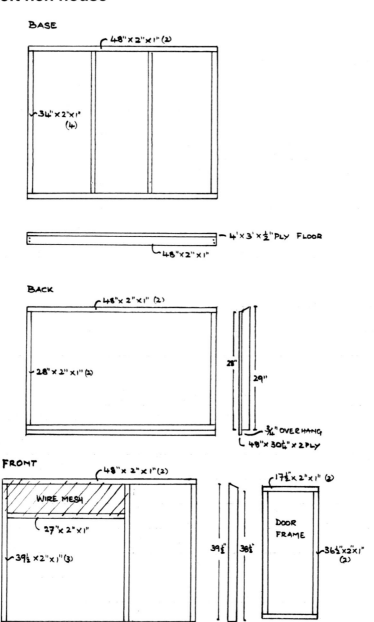

BASE

48" × 2" × 1" (2)

36" × 2" × 1" (4)

4' × 3' × ½" PLY FLOOR

48" × 2" × 1"

BACK

48" × 2" × 1" (2)

28" × 2" × 1" (2)

28"

29"

¾" OVERHANG

48" × 30¾" × 2 PLY

FRONT

48" × 2" × 1" (2)

WIRE MESH

27" × 2" × 1"

39½ × 2" × 1" (3)

39⅛"

38⅛"

17½" × 2" × 1" (2)

DOOR FRAME

36½" × 2" × 1" (2)

60

4ft x 3ft hen house continued

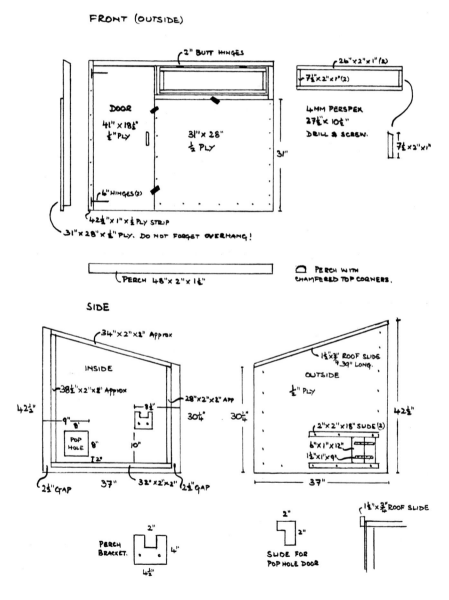

FRONT (OUTSIDE)

2" BUTT HINGES

26"x2"x1" (2)

7½"x2"x1"(2)

DOOR
41" x 18½"
½" PLY

31"x 28"
½ PLY

4 MM PERSPEX
27½"x 10½"
DRILL & SCREW.

31"

7½"x2"x1"

6" HINGES (2)

42½"x 1" x ½ PLY STRIP

31"x 28"x½" PLY. DO NOT FORGET OVERHANG!

PERCH 48"x 2"x 1½"

PERCH WITH CHAMFERED TOP CORNERS.

SIDE

34"x 2"x 2" Approx

INSIDE

38½"x 2"x 2" Approx

42½"

9"

POP HOLE

8"

12"

28"x2"x2" App

8½"

30¼"

10"

2½"GAP

37"

32"x2"x2"

2½"GAP

30¼"

1½x3" ROOF SLIDE
39" LONG.

OUTSIDE

½" PLY

42½"

2"x 2"x18" SLIDE (2)

6"x1"x12"

1½"x1"x9"

37"

PERCH BRACKET.

2"

4"

4½"

SLIDE FOR POP HOLE DOOR

2"

2"

1½"x3" ROOF SLIDE

61

4ft x 3ft hen house continued

SIDE

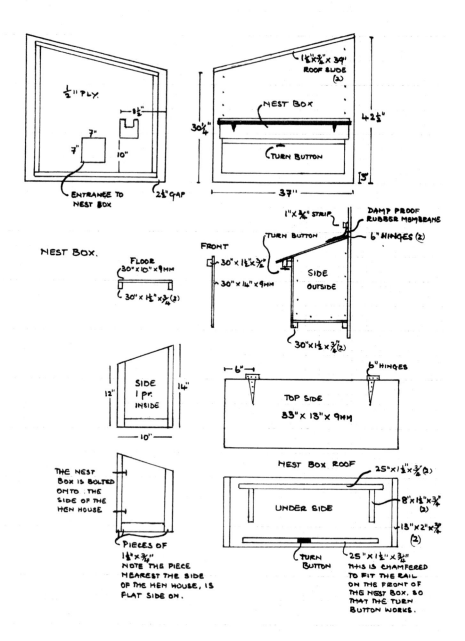

½" PLY.

1½"

7"

7"

10"

ENTRANCE TO
NEST BOX

2½" GAP

1⅛"x⅞" x 39"
ROOF SLIDE
(2)

NEST BOX

42½"

30¾"

TURN BUTTON

[3']

37"

1"x ¾" STRIP

DAMP PROOF
RUBBER MEMBRANE

FRONT

TURN BUTTON

6" HINGES (2)

NEST BOX.

FLOOR
30"x 10" x 9MM

30"x 1½"x ¾"

30" x 1½"x ¾" (2)

30" x 14" x 9MM

SIDE
OUTSIDE

30"x 1½ x ¾ (2)

6"

6" HINGES

12"

SIDE
1 pr.
INSIDE

14"

TOP SIDE

39"x 13"x 9MM

10"

NEST BOX ROOF

25"x 1½"x ¾"(2)

THE NEST
BOX IS BOLTED
ONTO THE
SIDE OF THE
HEN HOUSE

UNDER SIDE

8"x 1½"x ¾"
(2)

13"x2"x¾"
(2)

PIECES OF
1½"x ¾"
NOTE THE PIECE
NEAREST THE SIDE
OF THE HEN HOUSE, IS
FLAT SIDE ON.

TURN
BUTTON

25"x 1½"x ¾"
THIS IS CHAMFERED
TO FIT THE RAIL
ON THE FRONT OF
THE NEST BOX, SO
THAT THE TURN
BUTTON WORKS.

4ft x 3ft hen house continued

ROOF

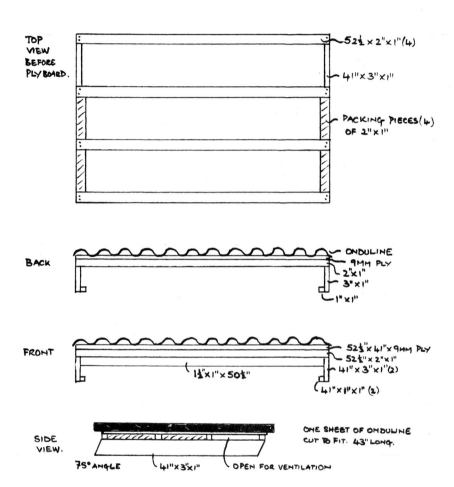

TOP VIEW BEFORE PLY BOARD.
- 52½ x 2" x 1" (4)
- 41" x 3" x 1"
- PACKING PIECES (4) OF 2" x 1"

BACK
- ONDULINE
- 9MM PLY
- 2" x 1"
- 3" x 1"
- 1" x 1"

FRONT
- 52½" x 41" x 9MM PLY
- 52½" x 2" x 1"
- 41" x 3" x 1" (2)
- 41" x 1" x 1" (2)
- 1½" x 1" x 50½"

SIDE VIEW.
- ONE SHEET OF ONDULINE CUT TO FIT. 43" LONG.
- 75° ANGLE
- 41" x 3" x 1"
- OPEN FOR VENTILATION

25 BIRD FREE RANGE HOUSE

This 8ft x 4ft house makes an excellent colony building for 25 laying hens such as Black Rocks. It would look wonderful with, say, a flock of Speckled Sussex or Exchequer Leghorns in residence.

I made a version of this house several years ago for my flock of Denderawis, an old Egyptian breed that we happened on in 1999. Since then I have modified the house and improved it, and I believe that the result is a good design for the birds, with plenty of access for cleaning, inspection and egg collecting.

The roof of this building is slightly larger to allow for under-eave ventilation; it is covered with half inch plyboard and topped with two pieces of galvanized box section iron. The Perspex hinged window has an adjustable catch and gives good light as well as extra ventilation. The leak- proof nestbox has a lid that slides back into the house, ensuring that the inside of the box stays dry, and there is a fox-proof catch securing it on the outside. The access door allows plenty of room for cleaning out the house and attending to food hoppers inside.

There is a flap on the outside of the house which opens upwards to reveal the end of a slide-out droppings board. This board is very easy to clean and should be done every 2 to 3 weeks. Simply slide it out, place it on the edge of a wheelbarrow and scrape the shavings and muck straight in. If you slightly moisten the fresh shavings before spreading them on the clean board you'll find that they stay in place well. You can use a watering can with a fine rose for the job and perhaps add a little Virkon or mild smelling disinfectant to the water as well. This method of cleaning means that the floor of the house will only need mucking out every 2 to 3 months.

The two perches in the house are both removable as well as being hinged so that they can be lifted out of the way when the floor is being cleaned. I have provided two pop holes which I have found to be infinitely better for the hens than one, if there is the space to do it; when there is a cold wet wind blowing at one side of the house, the hens can use the other pop hole without being buffeted about; also, the shavings on the floor don't get blown from one end of the house to the other. Both pop holes have fox-proof catches on the doors.

The house is on skids and can be moved round the field with a tractor.

25 bird free range house.

Skids for this house.

Detail of pull-out droppings board and pop hole.

Droppings board partially extended.

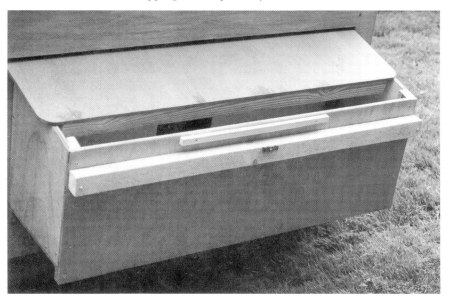

Detail of nest box lid.

Detail of perches.

25 bird house

FLOOR & SKIDS

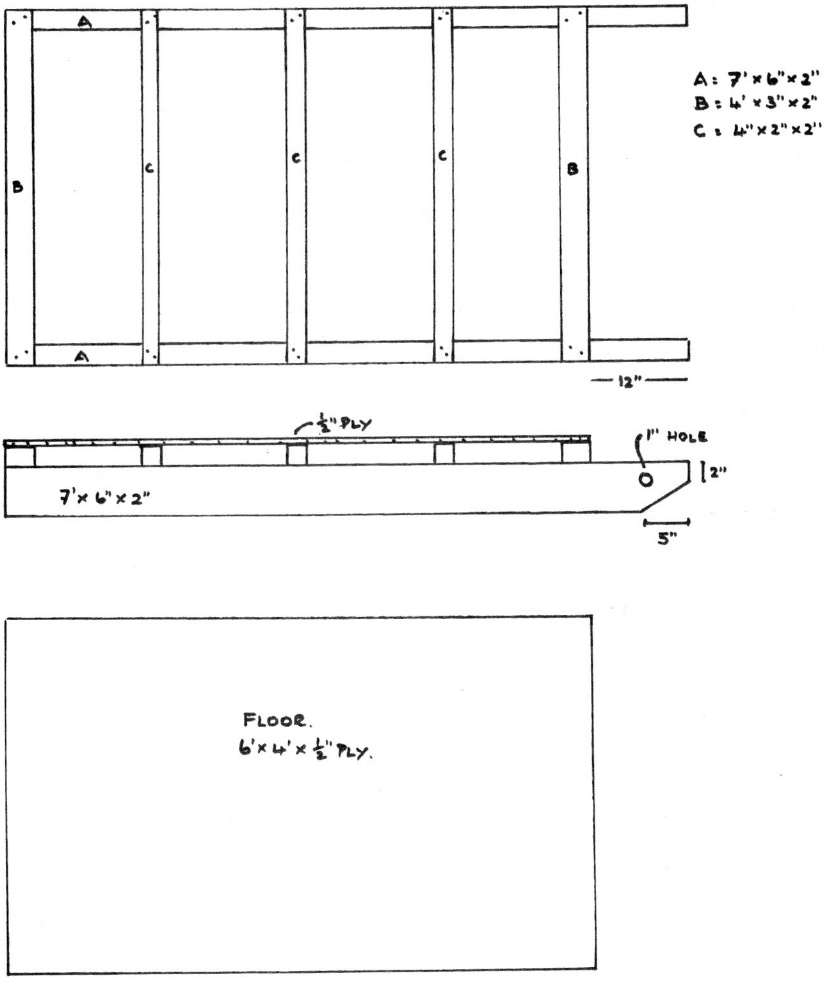

A: 7' × 6" × 2"
B: 4' × 3" × 2"
C: 4" × 2" × 2"

— 12" —

½" PLY

7' × 6" × 2"

1" HOLE

2"

5"

FLOOR.
6' × 4' × ½" PLY.

25 bird house continued

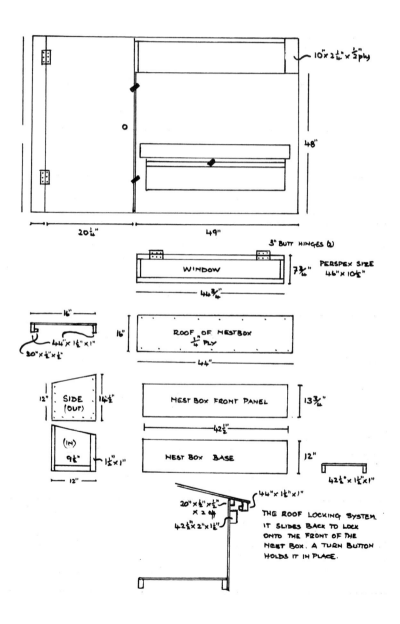

10" x 2¼" x ½" ply

48"

20¼"

49"

3" BUTT HINGES (2)

WINDOW

7¾"

PERSPEX SIZE
46" x 10½"

44¾"

16"

44" x 1½" x 1"

30" x ¼" x ¼"

16"

ROOF OF NESTBOX
¼" PLY

44"

12"   SIDE
(OUT)

14½"

NEST BOX FRONT PANEL

13¾"

(IN)
9¾"

1½" x 1"

42½"

NEST BOX BASE

12"

12"

42½" x 1½" x 1"

44" x 1½" x 1"

20" x ½" x ½"
x 2 off

42½" x 2" x 1½"

THE ROOF LOCKING SYSTEM.
IT SLIDES BACK TO LOCK
ONTO THE FRONT OF THE
NEST BOX. A TURN BUTTON
HOLDS IT IN PLACE.

70

25 bird house continued

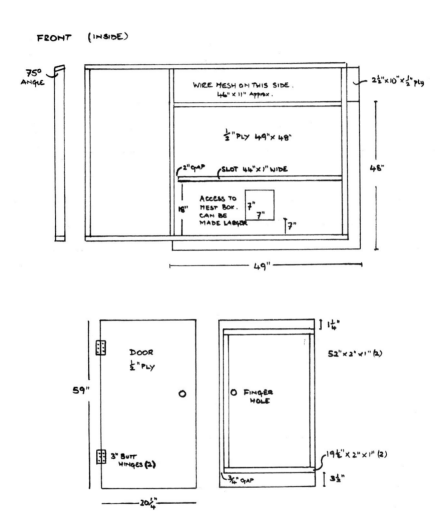

FRONT (INSIDE)

75° ANGLE

WIRE MESH ON THIS SIDE.
46" × 11" Approx.

$\frac{1}{2}$" PLY 49" × 48"

2$\frac{1}{2}$" × 10" × $\frac{1}{2}$" ply

48"

2" GAP   SLOT 46" × 1" WIDE

18"

ACCESS TO
NEST BOX.
CAN BE
MADE LARGER

7"
7"

7"

49"

DOOR
$\frac{1}{2}$" PLY

59"

3" BUTT
HINGES (2)

20$\frac{1}{4}$"

1$\frac{1}{4}$"

52" × 2" × 1" (2)

FINGER
HOLE

19$\frac{1}{2}$" × 2" × 1" (2)

3$\frac{1}{2}$"

$\frac{3}{4}$" GAP

SIDES

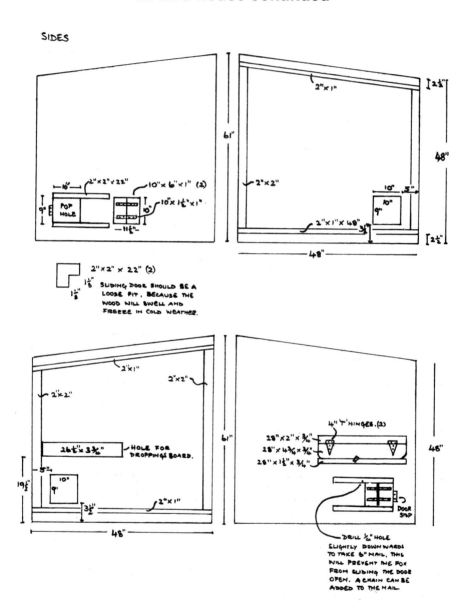

2"x2" x 22" (2)

SLIDING DOOR SHOULD BE A
LOOSE FIT, BECAUSE THE
WOOD WILL SWELL AND
FREEZE IN COLD WEATHER.

DRILL ½" HOLE
SLIGHTLY DOWNWARDS
TO TAKE 6" NAIL. THIS
WILL PREVENT THE FOX
FROM SLIDING THE DOOR
OPEN. A CHAIN CAN BE
ADDED TO THE NAIL.

25 bird house continued

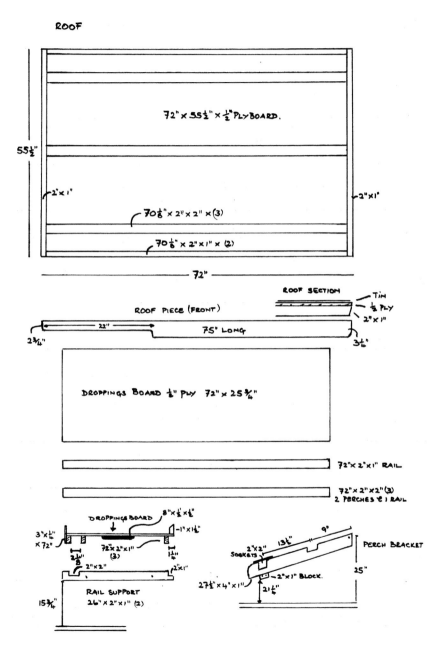

ROOF

$72" \times 55\frac{1}{2}" \times \frac{1}{2}"$ PLY BOARD.

$55\frac{1}{2}"$

$2" \times 1"$

$70\frac{1}{8}" \times 2" \times 2" \times (3)$

$70\frac{1}{8}" \times 2" \times 1" \times (2)$

$2" \times 1"$

$72"$

ROOF SECTION

TIN
$\frac{1}{2}$ PLY
$2" \times 1"$

ROOF PIECE (FRONT)

$22"$ $75'$ LONG

$2\frac{3}{4}"$ $3\frac{1}{8}"$

DROPPINGS BOARD $\frac{1}{2}"$ PLY $72" \times 25\frac{3}{4}"$

$72" \times 2" \times 1"$ RAIL

$72" \times 2" \times 2"$ (3)
2 PERCHES & 1 RAIL

DROPPINGS BOARD $8" \times \frac{1}{8}" \times \frac{1}{4}"$

$3" \times \frac{1}{4}"$
$\times 72"$ $1" \times 1\frac{1}{4}"$

$2\frac{1}{8}"$
$72" \times 2" \times 1"$ $1\frac{1}{4}"$
(3)

$2" \times 2"$ $2" \times 1"$

RAIL SUPPORT
$26" \times 2" \times 1"$ (2)

$15\frac{3}{4}"$

$2" \times 2"$
SOCKETS $13\frac{1}{2}"$ $9"$

$27\frac{1}{2}" \times 4" \times 1"$ $2" \times 1"$ BLOCK.

$21\frac{1}{4}"$

PERCH BRACKET

$25"$

73

25 bird house continued

BACK

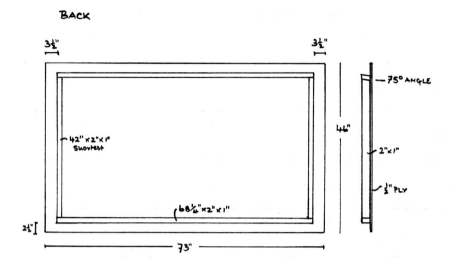

$3\frac{1}{2}"$

$3\frac{1}{2}"$

75° ANGLE

42" x 2" x 1"
Shortest

46"

2" x 1"

$\frac{1}{2}"$ PLY

$68\frac{1}{4}"$ x 2" x 1"

$2\frac{1}{2}"$

73"

50 BIRD FREE RANGE HOUSE

This 8ft x 6ft (240cms x 183cms) house would be ideal for someone who is keen to start a free range egg business. It is cheap to make, robust and easy to maintain. I do deplore the kind of situation where there is a huge building set in the middle of a field with hundreds of birds paddling about in a sea of mud. The beauty of this house is that as it's not too big it's easy to move so a muddy morass never has a chance to develop.

This house incorporates many excellent features such as large outside fox-proof nest boxes, a pull-out droppings board, two pop holes and three large skids for mobility. There is plenty of room, making cleaning out and egg collecting quick and easy. The perches are slightly raked, encouraging the first birds to roost to go to the top perch, leaving room for the late comers on the lower perch. There is plenty of light and

50 bird free range house.

75

adjustable ventilation in addition to air vents under the eaves. All the components in the house can be quickly and easily removed for cleaning and there is space for food hoppers.

The house can be moved round by tractor or four wheel drive vehicle.

Details of interior

Details of droppings board and pop hole.

Details of nest boxes.

50 bird free range house

ROOF

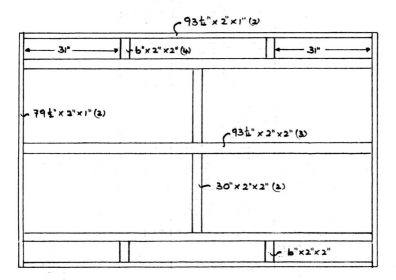

93½" x 2" x 1" (2)

31"

6"x 2"x2" (4)

31"

79½" x 2"x1" (2)

93½" x 2" x 2" (3)

30" x 2'x 2" (2)

6"x2"x2"

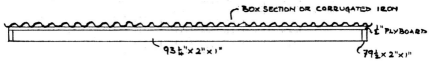

BOX SECTION OR CORRUGATED IRON

½" PLYBOARD

93½"x 2"x 1"

79½ x 2"x1"

½" PLYBOARD CLADDING UNDER THE IRON. USE UP OFF CUTS, AND
MAKE SURE THE JOINTS MEET IN THE CENTRES OF THE 2"x2"

50 bird free range house continued

FLOOR

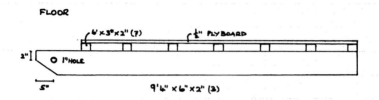

6'×3"×2" (7) $\frac{1}{2}$" PLYBOARD

2"]

O 1"HOLE

5"

9'6" × 6"×2" (3)

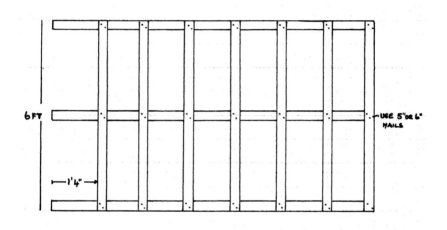

6FT

1'4"

USE 5" or 6" NAILS

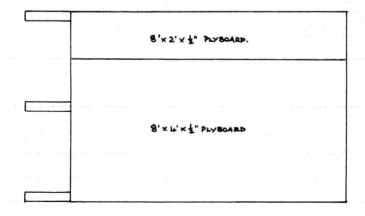

8'× 2'× $\frac{1}{2}$" PLYBOARD.

8'× 4'× $\frac{1}{2}$" PLYBOARD

80

50 bird free range house continued

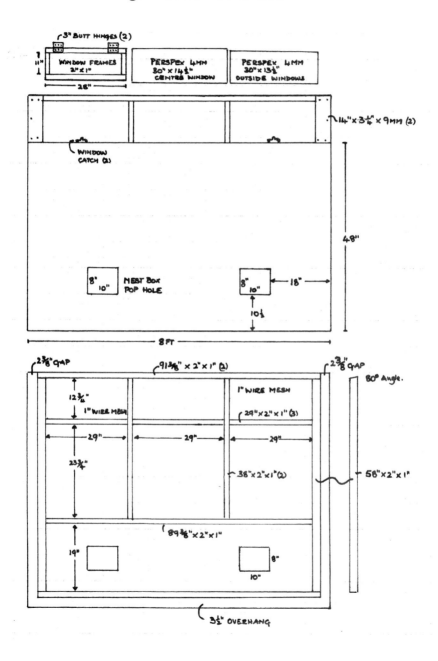

50 bird free range house continued

BACK.

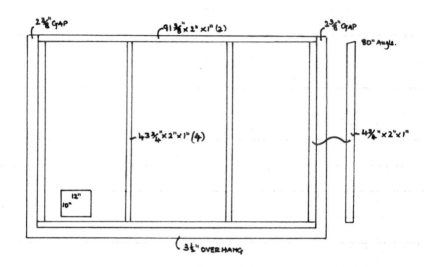

2⅜" GAP   91⅜"x2"x1" (2)   2⅜" GAP

80" Angle.

43¾"x2"x1" (4)

4¾"x2"x1"

12"
10"

3½" OVERHANG

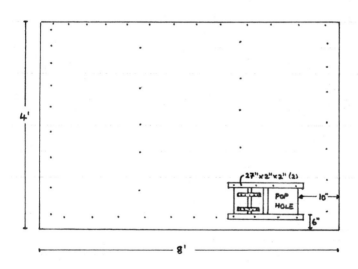

4'

27"x2"x2" (2)

POP HOLE   10"

6"

8'

50 bird free range house continued

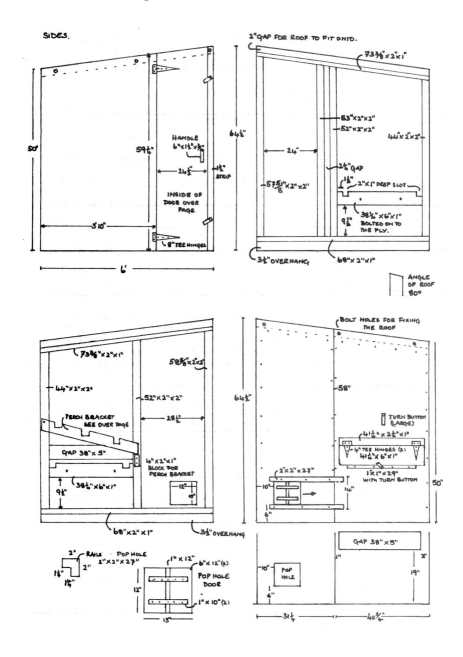

SIDES.

HANDLE
6"x1½"x¾"

59½"

24½"

1½"
STRIP

INSIDE OF
DOOR OVER
PAGE

50"

3' 10"

8" TEE HINGES

6'

64½"

2" GAP FOR ROOF TO FIT ONTO.

73⅜"x2"x1"

53"x2"x2"
52"x2"x2"

44½"x2"x2"

24"

2½" GAP

1½"
2"x1" DEEP SLOT

57⅝"x2"x2"

9½"
38½"x6"x1"
BOLTED ON TO
THE PLY.

3½" OVERHANG

68"x2"x1"

ANGLE
OF ROOF
80°

73⅜"x2"x1"

58⅝"x2"x2"

44½"x2"x2"

52"x2"x2"

PERCH BRACKET
SEE OVER PAGE

28½"

GAP 38"x 5"

4"x2"x1"
BLOCK FOR
PERCH BRACKET

38½"x6"x1"

9½"

12"
10"

68"x2"x1"

3½" OVERHANG

64½"

BOLT HOLES FOR FIXING
THE ROOF

58"

TURN BUTTON
(LARGE)

41½"x2½"x1"
4" TEE HINGES (2)
41½"x6"x1"

2"x2"x27"

1"x1"x29"
WITH TURN BUTTON

10"

14"

10"

6"

50"

2"
RAILS
1½"

2"
1½"

POP HOLE
2"x2"x27"

1"x12"
6"x12"(2)

POP HOLE
DOOR

12"

1"x10"(2)

13"

GAP 38"x5"

10"
POP
HOLE

1"

4"

2"

19"

31¼"

40¾"

50 bird free range house continued

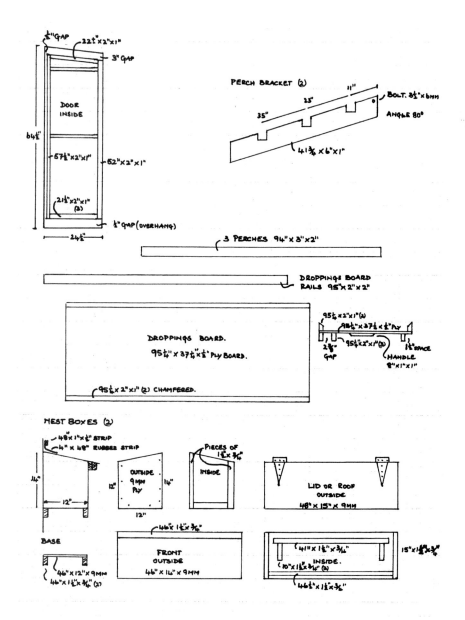

½" GAP
22½" x 2" x 1"
3" GAP

DOOR INSIDE

64½"

57½" x 2" x 1" 52" x 2" x 1"

2½" x 2" x 1" (2)

½" GAP (OVERHANG)

24½"

PERCH BRACKET (2)

11"
25"
35"

BOLT 2½" x 6MM
ANGLE 80°

41¾" x 6" x 1"

3 PERCHES 94" x 3" x 2"

DROPPINGS BOARD RAILS 95" x 2" x 2"

95½" x 2" x 1" (2)

DROPPINGS BOARD.
95½" x 37½" x ½" PLY BOARD.

95½" x 2" x 1" (2) CHAMFERED.

95½" x 37½" x ½" PLY
95½" x 2" x 1" (2)
2½" GAP
1½" SPACE
HANDLE 8" x 1" x 1"

NEST BOXES (2)

48" x 1" x ½" STRIP
4" x 48" RUBBER STRIP

14"

12"

OUTSIDE 9MM PLY
12"
14"

PIECES OF 1½" x ¾"

INSIDE

12"

LID OR ROOF OUTSIDE
48" x 15" x 9MM

BASE

46" x 12" x 9MM
46" x 1½" x ¾" (2)

46" x 1½" x ¾"

FRONT OUTSIDE
46" x 14" x 9MM

41" x 1½" x ¾"
10" x 1½" x ¾" (2)
INSIDE.
46½" x 1½" x ¾"

15" x 1½" x ¾"

SOUND MODERATED HOUSE

The remit of this house was to design and construct a building that would greatly reduce the sound of cockerels crowing, using readily available materials.

Several criteria had to be met: it was essential to have adequate light and ventilation, good access for birds and also humans (egg collecting and cleaning) and it had to be fairly simple to construct. As well as this it was important not to create a habitat that would be attractive to parasites (red mite etc) or encourage disease. All in all quite a tall order, but I think the results are acceptable.

This house does give people the opportunity to keep cockerels without annoying their neighbours during the night and early morning, although of course the cockerels will still crow when they are outside during the day.

The best way to muffle noise is to use extremely dense material, thus lead is excellent for sound proofing. It's not, however, very practical owing to its weight and prohibitive cost, so I have used sand. The walls of the building are constructed from a sandwich of .5" plyboard with a sand infill. Where it was not possible to use sand, in the ventilation shafts and roof, I

Sound Moderated House.

85

Ventilation Chimney.

have used Rockwool cavity insulation. Some people have asked why I didn't choose egg cartons, so frequently found in recording studios. The answer is that they would not last very long with the hens pecking at them and would gradually disintegrate if they got wet or damp.

I would like to thank Peter Ashford of Ian Sharland Ltd, Exeter, for his help and advice with this project.

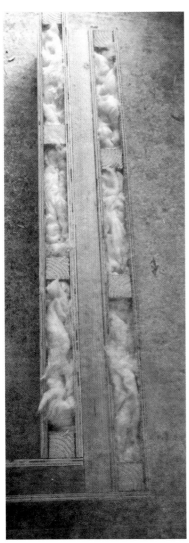

Detail of Ventilation Chimney.

Detail of Floor.

Interior showing perch.

Detail of interior.

Detail of pop hole

88

Sound moderated house

BASE

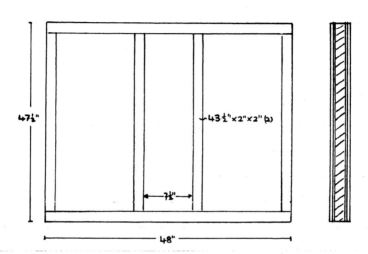

47½"

← 43½"×2"×2" (2)

7½"

48"

VENTILATION SHAFT

6"×5" Ply cover.

7½"×2"×2" with 15° angle.

6"×6"×½ Ply

6"×12⅜"
×½Ply

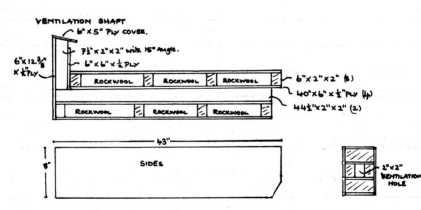

ROCKWOOL   ROCKWOOL   ROCKWOOL

ROCKWOOL   ROCKWOOL   ROCKWOOL

6"×2"×2" (3)

40"×6"×½"Ply (4)

44½"×2"×2" (2)

43"

SIDES

8"

2"×2"
VENTILATION
HOLE

Sound moderated house continued

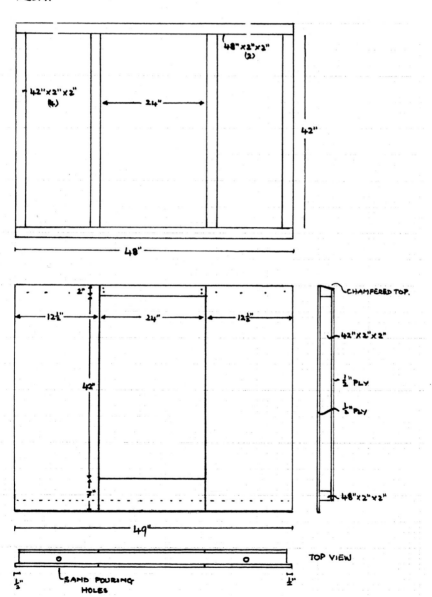

48" x 2" x 2"
(2)

42" x 2" x 2"
(4)

24"

42"

48"

CHAMPERED TOP.

42" x 2" x 2"

½" PLY

½" PLY

48" x 2" x 2"

2"

12¼"

24"

12⅛"

42"

7"

49"

TOP VIEW

SAND POURING HOLES

1½"

1½"

Sound moderated house continued

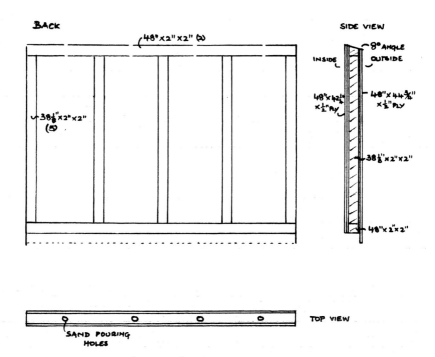

BACK

48"x2"x2" (2)

38⅛"x2"x2"
(5)

SIDE VIEW

8° ANGLE
INSIDE   OUTSIDE

48"x42⅛"
x½" PLY

48"x 44⅜"
x½" PLY

38⅛"x2"x2"

48"x 2"x2"

TOP VIEW

SAND POURING
HOLES

✳ USE PLAY SAND BECAUSE IT IS DRY AND POURS WELL.

Sound moderated house continued

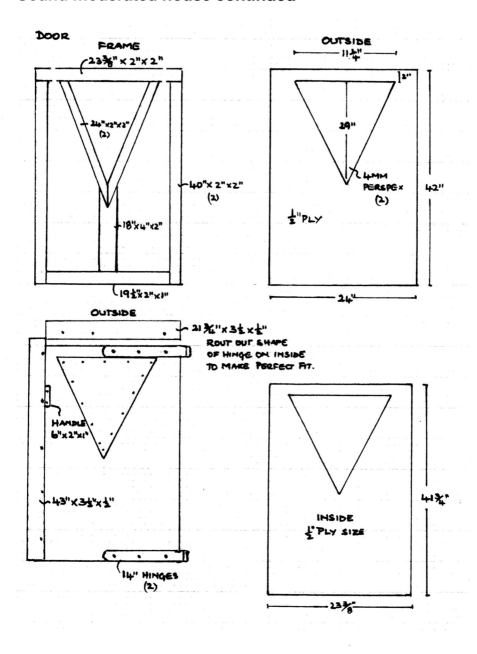

DOOR

FRAME

23⅜" × 2" × 2"

24"×2"×2" (2)

40"× 2"×2" (2)

18"×4"×2"

19½"×2"×1"

OUTSIDE

11¼"

2"

29"

4MM PERSPEX (2)

½"PLY

42"

24"

OUTSIDE

21⅞"×3½"×½"
ROUT OUT SHAPE
OF HINGE ON INSIDE
TO MAKE PERFECT FIT.

HANDLE
6"×2"×1"

43"×3½"×½"

14" HINGES (2)

INSIDE
½" PLY SIZE

41¾"

23⅜"

Sound moderated house continued

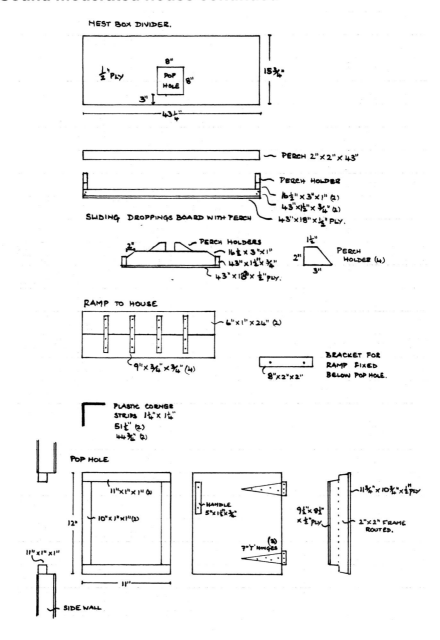

NEST BOX DIVIDER.

½" PLY

8"
POP HOLE 8"

3"

15¾"

43¼"

PERCH 2"×2"×43"

PERCH HOLDER
16½"×3"×1" (2)
43"×½"×¾" (2)
43"×18"×½" PLY.

SLIDING DROPPINGS BOARD WITH PERCH

2"

PERCH HOLDERS
16½×3"×1"
43"×1½"×¾"
43"×18"×½" PLY.

1½"
2"
3"

PERCH HOLDER (4)

RAMP TO HOUSE

6"×1"×24" (2)

9"×¾"×¾" (4)

8"×2"×2"

BRACKET FOR RAMP FIXED BELOW POP HOLE.

PLASTIC CORNER STRIPS 1¼"×1¼"
51¼" (2)
44¾" (2)

POP HOLE

11"×1"×1" (2)

10"×1"×1" (2)

12"

11"×1"×1"

11"

SIDE WALL

HANDLE
5"×1½"×¾"

7" T HINGES
(2)

9½"×9½"
×½" PLY

11¾"×10¾"×½" PLY

2"×2" FRAME ROUTED.

Sound moderated house continued

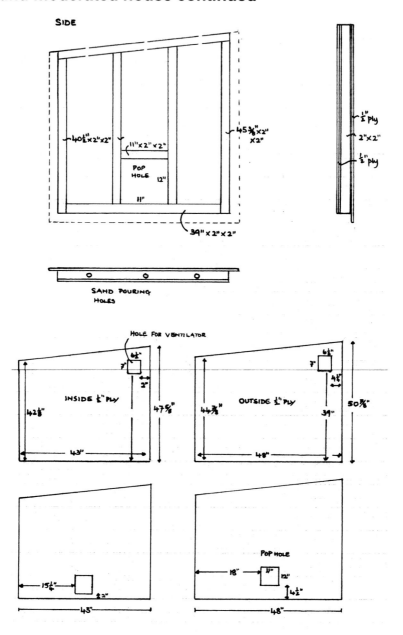

SIDE

SAND POURING HOLES

HOLE FOR VENTILATOR

INSIDE ½" PLY

OUTSIDE ½" PLY

POP HOLE

Sound moderated house continued

BASE (UNDERSIDE)

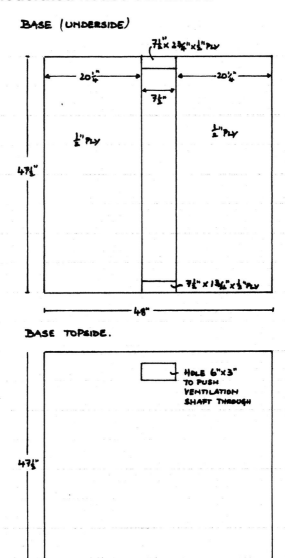

$7\frac{1}{2}$" x $2\frac{5}{8}$" x $\frac{1}{2}$" PLY

20$\frac{1}{4}$"

$7\frac{1}{2}$"

20$\frac{1}{4}$"

$\frac{1}{2}$" PLY

$\frac{1}{2}$" PLY

47$\frac{1}{4}$"

$7\frac{1}{2}$" x $1\frac{3}{4}$" x $\frac{1}{2}$" PLY

48"

BASE TOPSIDE.

HOLE 6"x3"
TO PUSH
VENTILATION
SHAFT THROUGH

47$\frac{1}{2}$"

48"

95

Sound moderated house continued

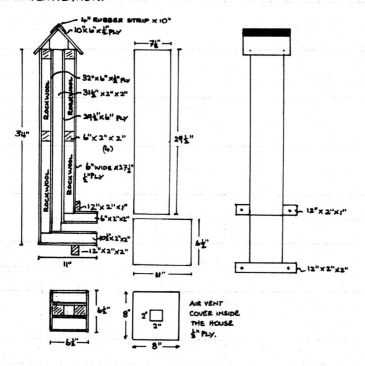

4" RUBBER STRIP × 10"
10"×6"×½" PLY
32"×6"×½" PLY
31½"×2"×2"
29½"×6" PLY
6"×2"×2" (4)
6" WIDE × 27½" ½" PLY
12"×2"×1"
6"×2"×2"
10½"×2"×2"
12"×2"×2"

34"
ROCKWOOL
ROCKWOOL
ROCKWOOL
ROCKWOOL

7½"
29½"
6½"
11"
11"

12"×2"×1"
12"×2"×2"

6½"
8"
2"
2"
6½"
8"

AIR VENT
COVER INSIDE
THE HOUSE
½" PLY.

ROOF

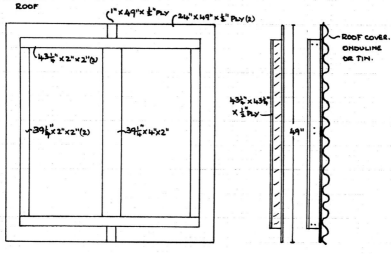

1"×49"×½" PLY
24"×49"×½" PLY (2)
43¼"×2"×2" (2)
39½"×2"×2" (2)
39¼"×4"×2"

ROOF COVER.
ONDULINE
OR TIN.

43¼"×43¼"
×½" PLY

49"

96

URBAN POULTRY HOUSE

This house is designed for the urban dweller who wants to keep 4 to 6 hens and enjoy proper fresh eggs.

The house is divided into two sections, a roosting and egg laying area and a daytime area for feeding, drinking and scratching about. Both parts are covered. You can shut the birds into either section by closing the pop hole door. The droppings board and perch slide forward to reveal the nestbox, and all these components can be taken out for quick and easy cleaning. Both front boards lift out as well, so you can push a wheelbarrow up against the house and scrape the floor and droppings board straight into it. Empty the wheelbarrow onto the compost heap when you've finished.

The litter in the house can be straw, shavings, dry peat or even shredded paper from the office, but don't use bark products as they may contain fungus.

You can feed your birds from a hopper inside the house, either mounted on the wall or hung from the ceiling; the water drinker is best hung from the ceiling as well to prevent it being knocked over or litter being scratched into it. Your birds will enjoy any vegetable scraps you can give them from the kitchen.

When you are at home working in the garden you can let your hens out to have a peck around, but remember, they are not good gardeners although they can become great companions. Don't forget to shut them in again at the end of the day!

Urban poultry house.

Urban poultry house with ramp down.

Details of interior of house.

99

Urban poultry house

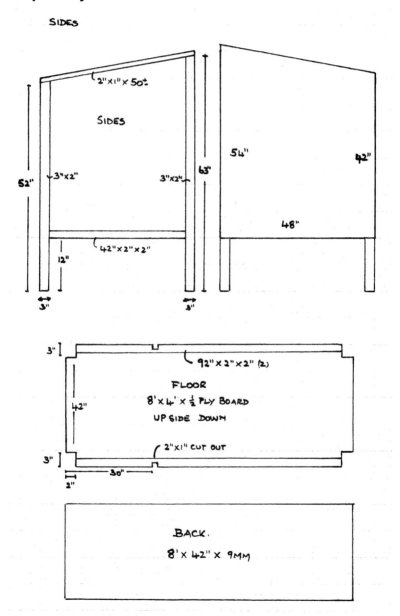

SIDES

2"×1" × 50½"

SIDES

52"

3"×2"

3"×2"

63"

54"

42"

48"

42"×2"×2"

12"

3"

3"

3"

92"×2"×2" (2)

FLOOR

8'×4' × ½ PLY BOARD

UPSIDE DOWN

42"

2"×1" CUT OUT

3"

30"

2"

BACK.

8'× 42" × 9MM

Urban poultry house continued

INSIDES

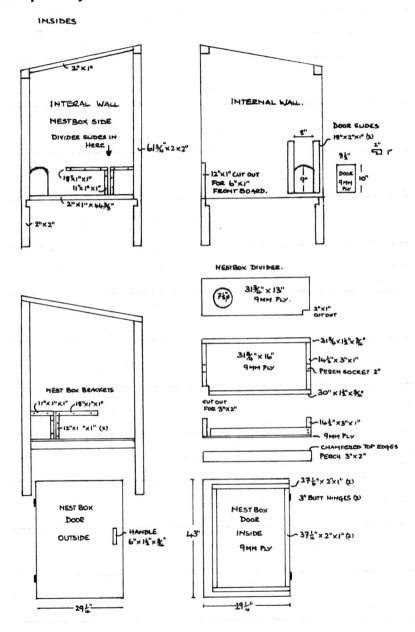

INTERAL WALL

NESTBOX SIDE

DIVIDER SLIDES IN HERE ↓

2"x1"

61¾"x2x2"

18½"x1"x1"
11½"x1"x1"

2"x1"x44⅜"

2"x2"

INTERNAL WALL.

8"

DOOR SLIDES
18"x2"x1" (2)

2"
1"

9½"

DOOR
9MM
PLY

10"

12"x1" CUT OUT
FOR 6"x1"
FRONT BOARD.

9"

NESTBOX DIVIDER.

7½"

31¾" x 13"
9MM PLY.

2"x1"
CUTOUT

31¾" x1½"x¾"

14½"x 3"x1"

PERCH SOCKET 2"

31¾" x 16"
9MM PLY

30" x 1½x¾"

CUT OUT
FOR 3"x2"

14½"x3"x1"

9MM PLY

CHAMFERED TOP EDGES
PERCH 3"x2"

NEST BOX BRACKETS

11"x1"x1"   18"x1"x1"

12"x1 "x1" (2)

NEST BOX
DOOR

OUTSIDE

HANDLE
6"x1½"x¾"

29¼"

27½"x 2"x1" (2)

3" BUTT HINGES (2)

NEST BOX
DOOR

INSIDE

9MM PLY

43"

37½"x 2"x1" (2)

29¼"

101

Urban poultry house continued

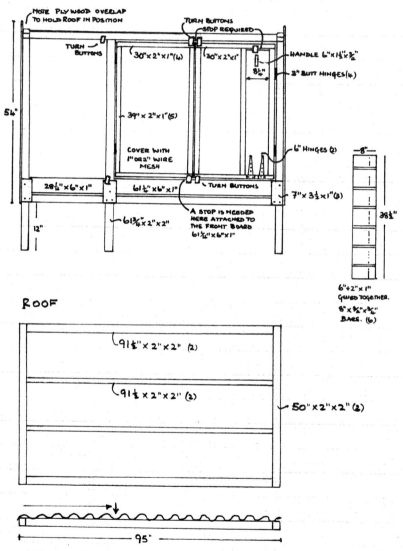

WHEELCHAIR USER'S POULTRY HOUSE

I designed this house with the help of Nigel Woodrup, a friend of mine who is confined to a wheelchair. I wanted to produce a house which could be managed by disabled people and would give them a chance to work with hens and enjoy a new hobby.

There are two large doors, one on each side of the house, which provide good access for cleaning out the inside with a dustpan and brush. I have put a low division down the middle of the floor, hoping that it will contain the dirtiest droppings under the perch, so that the other half of the floor won't need cleaning out so often. The nestbox should be easy to manage for egg collection or cleaning.

Front of house closed

As the house is raised on legs it provides a good sheltered area underneath where the birds can be fed and watered. There is a small opening into it for access which can be moved or enlarged if necessary.

You will need to have paving slabs laid round three sides of the house for the wheelchair. On the forth side there should be a securely fenced run for the hens that they can reach via a ramp. Once they are back inside the house at night you can shut them in by releasing the cord on the outside of the pop hole door.

Front of house open showing access.

Side view showing pop hole and ramp.

Wheelchair user's poultry house

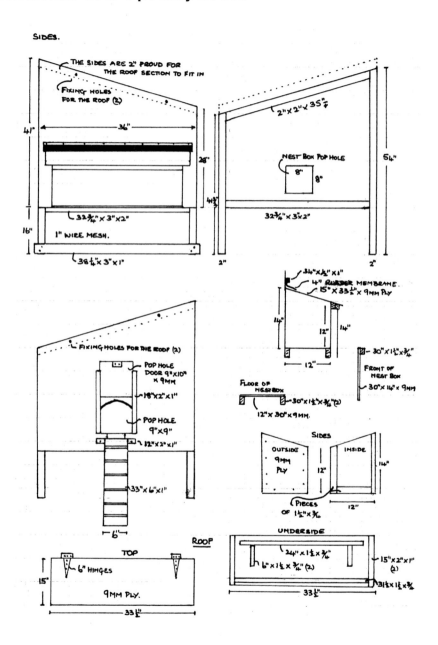

Wheelchair user's poultry house continued

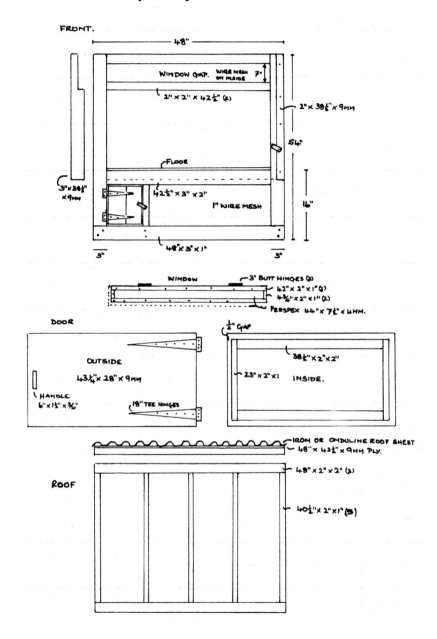

FRONT.

48"

WINDOW GAP. WIRE MESH ON INSIDE 7"

2" × 2" × 42½" (2)

2" × 38½" × 9mm

54"

FLOOR

3" × 38½" × 9mm

42½" × 3" × 2"

1" WIRE MESH

16"

3"   48" × 3" × 1"   3"

WINDOW   3" BUTT HINGES (2)
42" × 2" × 1" (2)
4¾" × 2" × 1" (2)
PERSPEX 44" × 7½" × 4MM.

DOOR   ½ GAP

OUTSIDE   38½" × 2" × 2"

43¼" × 28" × 9mm   23" × 2" × 1   INSIDE.

HANDLE
6" × 1½" × ¾"   18" TEE HINGES

IRON OR ONDULINE ROOF SHEET
48" × 42½" × 9MM PLY.

48" × 2" × 2" (2)

ROOF

40½" × 2" × 1" (3)

Wheelchair user's poultry house continued

BACK

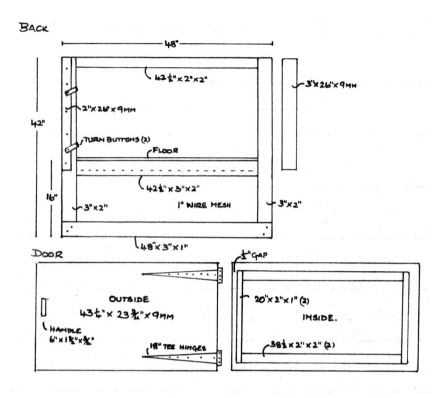

48"	
42½" x 2" x 2"	3' x 26' x 9mm
2" x 26' x 9mm	
42"	
TURN BUTTONS (2)	
FLOOR	
16"	
42½" x 3" x 2"	
3" x 2"	1" WIRE MESH	3" x 2"
48" x 3" x 1"	

DOOR

OUTSIDE	½" GAP
43¼" x 23¾" x 9mm	20" x 2" x 1" (2)
HANDLE 6" x 1½" x ¾"	INSIDE.
18" TEE HINGES	38½ x 2" x 2" (2)

FLOOR

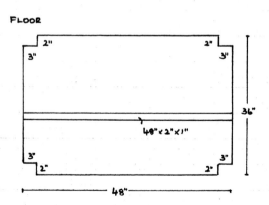

2"	2"
3"	3"
	36"
48" x 2" x 1"	
3"	3"
2"	2"
48"	

108

SHELTERS

Having studied our flock I have noticed an additional need for shelter outside their houses. This will give protection from the weather and winged predators, and should be dry underfoot and provide an area for dust-bathing and feeding. It seems that the hens don't want to use their houses during the day time, perhaps because they consider them to be egg-laying and sleeping areas only, hence the need for additional shelter. I have since found that our lambs rather like to use them as well. I offer two types, one fairly basic and the other one mobile and incorporating a dust-bath and treadle feeder.

Small shelter.

Large shelter.

Small shelter

SMALL SHELTER.

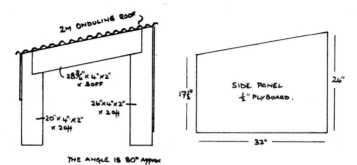

2M ONDULINE ROOF

28¾" × 4" × 2"
× 3 OFF

26" × 4" × 2"
× 2 OFF

20" × 4" × 2"
× 2 OFF

THE ANGLE IS 80° Approx

SIDE PANEL
¼" PLYBOARD.

17½"

24"

32"

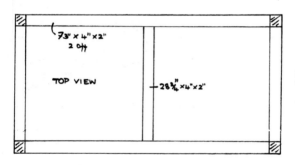

73" × 4" × 2"
2 OFF

TOP VIEW

28¾" × 4" × 2"

I HAVE USED A 2M
LENGTH OF ONDULINE FOR
THE ROOF. IF YOU USE A
CORRUGATED METAL SHEET,
YOU MAY HAVE TO ADJUST
THE WIDTH AND THE LENGTH
OF 4" × 2" FRAME.

BACK PANEL
77½" × 24"

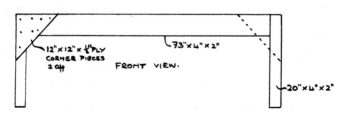

12" × 12" × ¼" PLY
CORNER PIECES
2 OFF

73" × 4" × 2"

FRONT VIEW.

20" × 4" × 2"

Large shelter

Detail of wheel assembly.

Treadle feeder inside shelter.

111

Large shelter

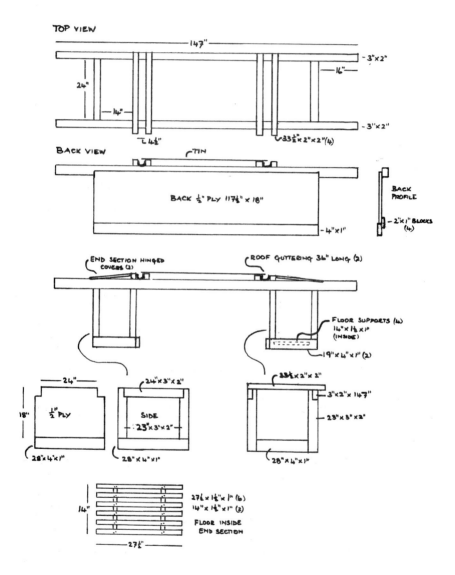

TOP VIEW
147"
24"
14"
~ 3"x2"
16"
~ 3"x2"
4½"
33½"x2"x2"(4)

BACK VIEW
TIN
BACK ½" PLY 117½" x 18"
BACK PROFILE
~ 2"x 1" BLOCKS (4)
~ 4"x1"

END SECTION HINGED COVERS (2)
ROOF GUTTERING 36" LONG (2)
FLOOR SUPPORTS (4) 16"x 1½ x 1" (INSIDE)
19"x 4"x 1" (2)

24"
24"x3"x 2"
23½"x2"x 2"
3"x2"x 147"
18"
½" PLY
SIDE 23"x3"x2"
23"x 3"x2"
28"x4"x1"
28"x 4"x1"
28"x 4"x1"

14"
27½ x 1½"x 1" (6)
14"x 1½"x 1" (3)
FLOOR INSIDE END SECTION
27½"

Large shelter continued

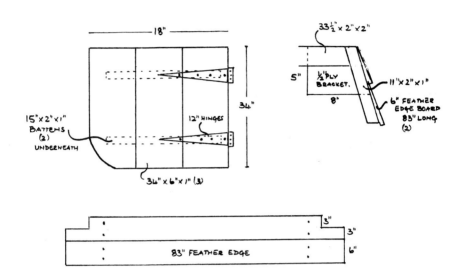

15"x2"x1"
BATTENS
(2)
UNDERNEATH

18"

34"

12" HINGES

34" x 6" x 1" (3)

33½" x 2" x 2"

5"   ½" PLY
        BRACKET.

8"

11" x 2" x 1"

6" FEATHER
EDGE BOARD
83" LONG
(2)

3"

3"

6"

83" FEATHER EDGE

Large shelter showing access.

113

ROLL AWAY NESTBOXES

I have battled with this idea for years and experimented with various designs and materials. Most commercial products are made of plastic or metal for easy cleaning, and it's hard to believe that hens actually use them, but I suppose they have no choice. I do know that they will refuse to lay in roll aways (sounds like some kind of cigarette!) if they are already using the more normal kind. To be successful you must introduce your hens to this type of nestbox before they come into lay.

The system I am using incorporates my own ideas and those of an old friend, Arthur Jennings from Salford in Warwickshire. Arthur produced a range of poultry equipment and incubators, together with a sex-linked commercial white Leghorn which laid brown eggs! Sadly he is dead now but he used to be a fount of information on the subject of poultry, and we discussed roll aways on many occasions.

One of the problems with this nestbox was deciding on suitable materials, in particular for the laying platform. I ended up using a rubber door mat upside down, as they are durable, washable and easily available.

Eggs can be collected from either the front or the back simply by turning the trays round; this means that once the nestbox is incorporated into the house the eggs can be collected from either inside or outside.

You will need a higher level of carpentry skills when you are making this nestbox to ensure that everything fits and works properly.

Side view of roll-away nest boxes showing removable top.

Front view of roll-away nest boxes.

Interior of roll-away nest boxes.

Above: Details of laying trays.

Left: Nest boxes closed.

Roll-away nest boxes

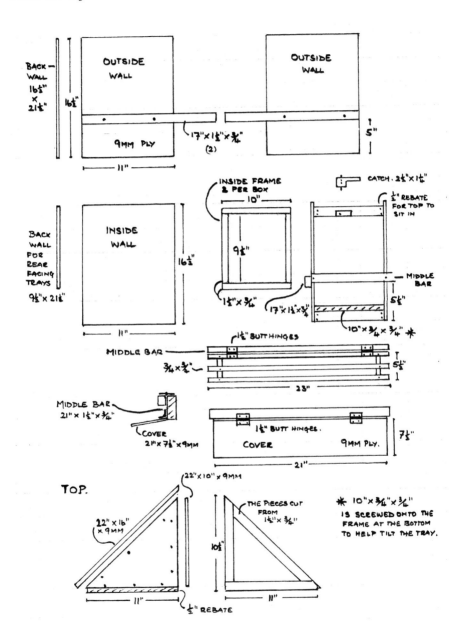

BACK WALL 16½" x 21½"

OUTSIDE WALL

OUTSIDE WALL

16½"

9MM PLY

17" x 1½" x ¾" (2)

5"

11"

BACK WALL FOR REAR FACING TRAYS 9½" x 21½"

INSIDE WALL

16½"

11"

INSIDE FRAME 2 PER BOX

10"

9¼"

1½" x ¾"

17" x 1½" x ¾"

CATCH. 2½" x 1½"

½" REBATE FOR TOP TO SIT IN

MIDDLE BAR

5½"

10" x ¾" x ¾" ✳

MIDDLE BAR

1½" BUTT HINGES

¾" x ¾"

5½"

23"

MIDDLE BAR 21" x 1½" x ¾"

COVER 21" x 7½" x 9MM

1½" BUTT HINGES.

COVER

9MM PLY.

7½"

21"

TOP.

22" x 10" x 9MM

22" x 16" x 9MM

THE PIECES CUT FROM 1½" x ¾"

10½"

11"

11"

½" REBATE

✳ 10" x ¾" x ¾" IS SCREWED ONTO THE FRAME AT THE BOTTOM TO HELP TILT THE TRAY.

Roll-away trays

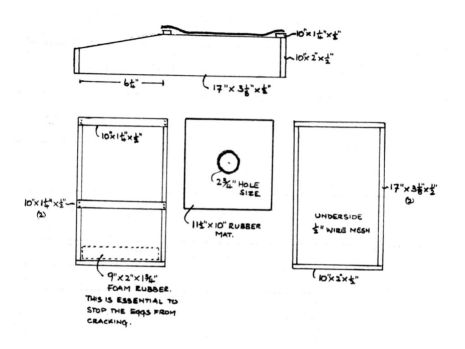

10"x1¼"x¼"

10"x 2"x½"

6¼"

17"x 3⅛"x¼"

10"x1¼"x¼"

10"x1¼"x½"
(2)

9"x2"x1¾"
FOAM RUBBER.
THIS IS ESSENTIAL TO
STOP THE EGGS FROM
CRACKING.

2¾" HOLE
SIZE

11½"x10" RUBBER
MAT.

UNDERSIDE
½" WIRE MESH

17"x3⅛"x½"
(2)

10"x2"x¼"

6FT RUN

In my book 'Poultry House Construction I have included an 8ft run. This one is smaller but has roof frames that can be slid open or taken off. It is very useful when you are catching birds as you can drive them inside and hold them there by blocking the opening with an up-ended frame. It is quick and easy to make.

6' run showing movable roof sections.

Run with hens held at one end using upended roof section..

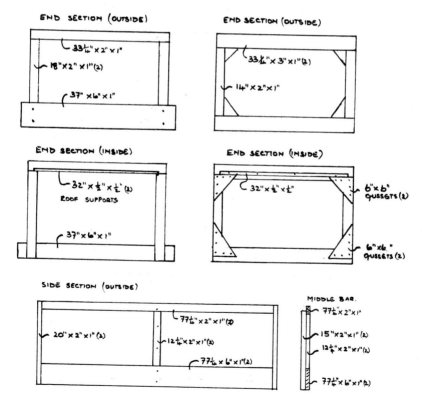

END SECTION (OUTSIDE)

33½" x 2" x 1"

18" x 2" x 1" (2)

37" x 6" x 1"

END SECTION (OUTSIDE)

33½" x 3" x 1" (2)

14" x 2" x 1"

END SECTION (INSIDE)

32" x ½" x ½" (2)
ROOF SUPPORTS

37" x 6" x 1"

END SECTION (INSIDE)

32" x ½" x ½"

6" x 6" GUSSETS (2)

6" x 6" GUSSETS (2)

SIDE SECTION (OUTSIDE)

20" x 2" x 1" (2)

77½" x 2" x 1" (2)

12½" x 2" x 1" (2)

77½" x 6" x 1" (2)

MIDDLE BAR.

77½" x 2" x 1"

15" x 2" x 1" (2)

12½" x 2" x 1" (2)

77½" x 6" x 1" (2)

6ft run

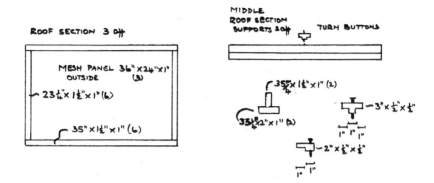

ROOF SECTION 3 Off

MESH PANEL 36"×24"×1"
OUTSIDE   (3)

23¼"×1½"×1" (6)

35"×1½"×1" (6)

MIDDLE
ROOF SECTION
SUPPORTS 20Off   TURN BUTTONS

35¾"×1½"×1" (2)

33¼"×2"×1" (2)

3"×½"×½"
1" 1" 1"

2"×½"×½"
1" 1"

TOP VIEW OF RUN WITHOUT ROOF SECTIONS

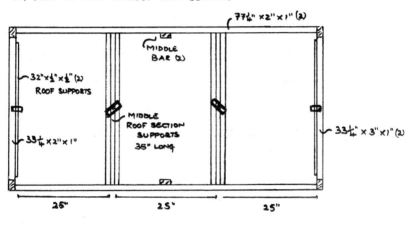

77½"×2"×1" (2)

MIDDLE
BAR (2)

32"×½"×½" (2)
ROOF SUPPORTS

MIDDLE
ROOF SECTION
SUPPORTS
35" LONG

33¼"×2"×1"

33¼"×3"×1" (2)

25"   25"   25"

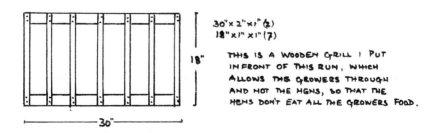

18"

30"

30"×2"×1" (2)
18"×1"×1" (7)

THIS IS A WOODEN GRILL I PUT
IN FRONT OF THIS RUN, WHICH
ALLOWS THE GROWERS THROUGH
AND NOT THE HENS, SO THAT THE
HENS DON'T EAT ALL THE GROWERS FOOD.

6FT AND 10FT SECTIONS

I have found these sections to be invaluable, not only for temporary pens for call ducks or bantams etc, but also for making exhibition pens at shows; you can join them together very quickly and easily with electric fencing wire and a staple gun to make a pen of any size. Just be careful not to split the wood when you nail up the frames.

If you want to use these sections for pheasants you should increase the height to 5 or 6ft and use 2" x 1" rather than 1.5" x .75". Knock some felt nails three quarters of the way in along the top rails and hook some nylon netting over them to form a covered pen. If this is going to be a

6' section with door closed.

122

permanent enclosure, make sure you look out for dead leaves or snow gathering on the top, and always clear it off to avoid the sections breaking under the weight.

10ft is about the maximum length for a section; any more and they become rather bendy and heavy to handle. Try to avoid using timber with large knots for the rails; they would make weak points in the construction and you would have to replace them eventually.

6' section with door open.

Detail of other side of section.

6ft section

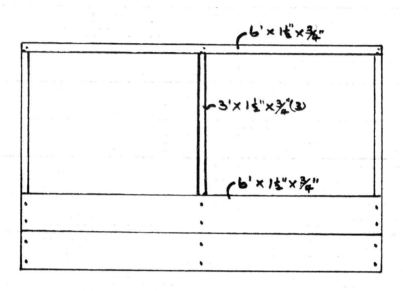

6' × 1⅝" × ¾"

3' × 1⅝" × ¾"(3)

6' × 1⅝" × ¾"

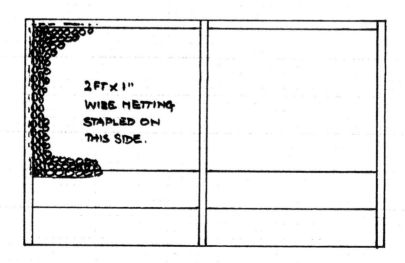

2FT × 1"
WIRE NETTING
STAPLED ON
THIS SIDE.

10ft section

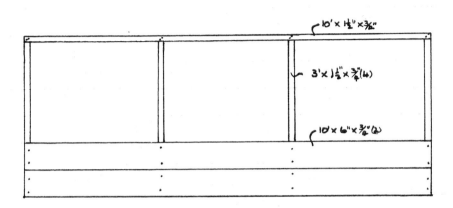

10' × 1½" × 3/2"

3' × 1½" × 3/4" (4)

10' × 6" × 3/4" (2)

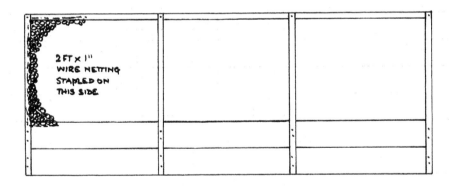

2 FT × 1"
WIRE NETTING
STAPLED ON
THIS SIDE

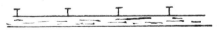

FELT NAILS ON THE TOP RAIL
FOR USE WITH NETTING.

6ft section with gate

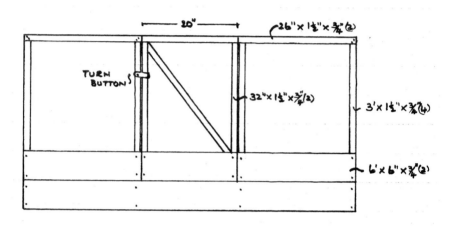

├── 20" ──┤
26"×1½"×¾" (2)

TURN BUTTON

32"×1½"×¾" (2)

3'×1½"×¾" (4)

6'×6"×¾" (2)

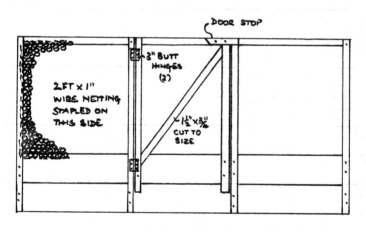

DOOR STOP

3" BUTT HINGES (2)

2FT×1" WIRE NETTING STAPLED ON THIS SIDE

1½"×¾" CUT TO SIZE